POD ALMIGHTY

POD ALMIGHTY!

The Autobiography of Dave Podmore
As told to Christopher Douglas,
Nick Newman and Andrew Nickolds

SIMON & SCHUSTER

LONDON · SYDNEY · NEW YORK · TOKYO · SINGAPORE · TORONTO

First published in Great Britain by
Simon & Schuster Ltd, 1996
A Viacom Company

Simon & Schuster Ltd
West Garden Place
Kendal Street
London W2 2AQ

Simon & Schuster of Australia Pty Ltd
Sydney

A CIP catalogue record for this book is available
from the British Library

ISBN 0-684-81761-6

Dave Podmore wishes it to be known that any unwarranted
or otherwise libellous rubbishings is entirely the fault of the
ghostwriters who didn't submit the text of their articles to him
beforehand, and that therefore he can't be held responsible for any
of it. Except the stuff about the Selectors, which is fair comment.

Typeset by Hewer Text Composition Services, Edinburgh

Printed and bound in Great Britain by
Butler & Tanner Ltd, Frome and London

David Podmore
Dedicates This Book To
THE HONEST TRUNDLER*

and any cricketer who shares
with him the motto
'Life – get the most out of it.'

*Together with my Business Manager, Ray Poole, I am currently considering investing in a chain of themed pub/restaurants, provisionally called The Honest Trundler and situated adjacent to the motorway system. Somewhere the weary professional would be guaranteed a warm welcome, a hot curry and something stronger, all at cricketer-friendly prices!

Pod enjoys a 'Champagne Moment'.
(Reproduced by kind permission of the *Leicester Mercury*)

Contents

Foreword

I still can't believe it. Twenty-three seasons in county cricket and still trundling! Who would have thought I'd still be putting it 'there or thereabouts' at my age? Who would have thought I'd still be squirting singles and relishing the cauldron of a diarrhoea finish just as much as when I was an apprehensive débutant?

What an honour it's been to play this great game. What a privilege to have done so for eight different counties. And what a pleasure to be enjoying another year's trouble-free motoring courtesy of Ray Poole (Nissan) of Hinckley, the East Midlands' premier saloon and light commercial distributor.

Obviously you can't go on for ever, but while there's still a demand for the more mature player who carries a ton of experience around with him then I'll keep drawing my pay. And what a pay-packet it's been; stuffed with friendships, memories, hilarious escapades in hotel corridors with the likes of Lamby, Gatt and Beef, and by-no-means-infrequent beverages with a certain gentleman whose name is not unadjacent to D. Gower Esquire. I own a beautiful detached home, I've got five dogs and I've appeared on *A Question of Sport* with Ian Botham. What more could you want? And now, to cap it all, I've been given the nod to write my own autobiography. Well, all you can say is, it's like a Boys' Own fairytale dream come true.

Regrets? None whatsoever. I'm not saying there haven't been bad times along with the good because there have. Sometimes I've been so disappointed with the way I've been treated I've totally lost faith in the human race to be honest. There are people running this game who couldn't spell the word 'integrity' if Carol Vorderman gave them the letters on a silver salver. But I'll leave all that for the main part of the book, along with my views on politics, neatness, the Pakistanis and how proper marketing could make this game great again.

You can sum up my love affair with cricket in one sentence: it's been one Champagne Moment after another. If I could do it all over again I wouldn't change a thing. Actually, champagne blows me up so I prefer to drink something a bit less gassy like a draught Bass or a sweet liqueur, but if ever there was an occasion for lighting up a panatella and cracking open a bottle of bubbly this would be it.

If you have a quarter of the fun reading *Pod Almighty* as I've had being Pod Almighty then, believe me, I envy you.

Your very good health!

1

IT'S BEEN A FAIRYTALE!

The year: 1987. The place: Sydney. Fifth Test, last day. It's ninety-two in the shade, the historic ground is bursting at the seams and the Aussies need four to win. *Crack*! The ball goes screaming through the covers where Dave Podmore makes a despairing dive towards it. At the end of his outstretched arm he feels a sudden pain like the sting of a bullet wound. He rolls in agony but before he can open his eyes his eardrums ring to the sound of sixty thousand shattered hopes.

Amid the chaotic, stump-grabbing scramble for the pavilion, he hears the words he will remember for the rest of his life, words which will echo down the annals of the game: 'Bloody hell, Pod! Now look what you've done. You've only gone and won us the ——ing Ashes!'

I must have played that scene a thousand times over in my mind and I still can't believe it never happened. But it didn't and it probably never will now because, let's face it, there's one set of rules for those whose faces happen to fit and another set for those who run into the same brick wall of unfairness time and time again. As to whether the Selectors have got things right over the last ten years, well, I'll let others be the judge of that.

But Dave Podmore wouldn't have it any other way. Not being a regular member of the England squad has been the greatest Christmas present anyone could ever wish for. Why? Because it's given me twenty-three of the most rewarding years in the most fantastic work-place in the world, namely county cricket.

It amazes me when people ask, 'Aren't you disappointed not to have had a bit more of a test career, Pod?' Well, from where I'm standing it doesn't seem very disappointing to have been awarded a handsome benefit by each of the eight counties I have had the honour to represent. It doesn't seem very disappointing to have a £228,000 nest egg sitting in the bank. It doesn't seem very disappointing to see an 'M' reg. Nissan Bluebird Premium sitting in the carport. If being able to afford a brand new kennel complex (costing £18,000) finished in lapped cedar is disappointing, then I'd be disappointed not to be disappointed.

I've done pretty well out of the game, I won't pretend I haven't. On the contrary, I'm bloody proud of it! I may not have had the recognition I deserve but I can hold up my head in any company and if anyone thinks they're better than me they want to take a look at our way of life. And if they've still got ideas after that, they should see the number of functions Jacqui and myself have been asked to attend over the next few months. They will find the invitations on the mantelpiece – just below the individually-framed facsimiles of my benefit cheques.

Who would have thought that the shy nineteen-year-old who was rejected by Derbyshire seconds all those years ago would one day move in a world of sponsored cars, Moat House receptions and black-tie celebrity raffles; a world where you can rub shoulders with the likes of Geoff Capes and Nookie Bear and think nothing of it; a world where you're on nickname terms with Lamby, Goochie, Broady and Emburey-ey; a world where you can take a complimentary document wallet or a port-and-stilton presentation box in your stride? All in all, not a bad return for an ordinary lad from Mansfield!

It has been a long, long road from Number 15 Foundry Lane to where I am now. Admittedly, it isn't all that far in distance terms – you just go straight through Sutton-in-Ashfield, then it's thirty minutes down the motorway, A563 for a couple of miles and wallop – you're in Oadby. But as far as lifestyle goes, it's on a different galaxy and when I go back now I'm a stranger, sadly.

It would be a bit of a cliché to say that cricket has been good to Dave Podmore. It wouldn't really be the whole story either because, let's be fair, Dave Podmore has been very good indeed to cricket. Ask any of the lucky lads who have attended the Dave Podmore Academy of Cricket (which will be open for business again the moment we get the nod from the Lottery fund). You won't catch those boys saying Dave Podmore's not prepared to put a bit back.

Ask anyone on the county circuit and they will tell you that D. V. Podmore is never prepared to give it anything less than the kitchen sink in the interests of his side, be that side Leicestershire, be it Derbyshire, be it Notts, be it Glamorgan, be it Gloucestershire, be it Sussex, be it Northants, be it Leicester again, be it Somerset and almost certainly next season, be it Durham. I have never put in less than 110%. More often than not I'll give it 200% and Merv Kitchen swears blind he saw me give 1001% at Ilkeston once and I can believe it. I'll leave it to the mathematicians to work out exactly how much commitment that comes to, but you can take it from me, if the skipper was a flaming cock-eyed woodlouse I'd die for him, and that's fact!

It sickens me when people say Dave Podmore only plays for a county until he gets a benefit and then moves on somewhere else. That kind of ignorance just makes me smile I'm afraid. The way I see it, playing for nine counties represents a hell of a commitment to English cricket. I'd like to see one or two of the current England crop display that kind of simple patriotism, to be frank. How many counties has Chris Lewis actually played for? (Think about it.)

I've given everything to this game and even though it's run by a fairly unpleasant kind of blocked drain which calls itself the TCCB – who personally I wouldn't blow my nose on if their kids were on fire – it is still the greatest game in the world and I'll probably end up playing it till I drop. People say, 'Come on Pod, you've had eight benefits amounting to a tidy £228,000, you're right for life, you've just won a brand new set of Duraflex ladders for your bowling in the Cost-cutter Cup last season, why don't you pack it in?' Do you suppose that Beethoven stopped composing symphonies just because he'd reached a situation whereby he could point to his record in the book and allow his figures to do the talking for him? Of course he didn't and it's the same with myself.

I keep going because I have to, because it gives me a thrill and because it gives me a buzz (I don't know if I've mentioned this but it also gives me a superbly reliable car supplied by Ray Poole (Nissan) of Hinckley. Nice people – nice prices!).

5

Who knows what Dave Podmore has yet to achieve in the game? Sure, it would be nice to score a hundred, or even a fifty, and, good grief, wouldn't it be the icing on the cake to take five wickets? But I may only have another four or five seasons left in the tank so you have to be realistic about personal goals. Whatever the future holds though, I can tell you one thing for sure, Dave Podmore will certainly be going for plenty of 'runs' next season in a Ray Poole Nissan!

THE DAVE PODMORE MASTERCLASS

2

EARLY DOORS

As I say, I haven't had it easy, not by any means. And it's been like that from the word go to be honest. There was never much money around when I was a lad. I was picked on at school and quite often thrashed with a cane for things I hadn't done – which is exactly as it should be, in my opinion. Pity more kids aren't brought up that way.

Nowadays it's all video games and Internet carry-on which is no sort of training for county cricket. That's probably why we're seeing all this ball-tampering; players lifting the seam with pen-knives and what have you. We used to have to make do with the neck of a broken ginger beer bottle. It is pitiful.

As I say, Fairness wasn't on the syllabus at Hard Knocks Secondary, Mansfield. My mum and dad drummed it into me that if you want money you're going to have to work for it and, what's more, you're going to have to work a bloody sight harder than the likes of M. J. K. Brearley and the rest of the silver spoon brigade. Those lessons have been worth a fortune to me.

To be precise, £228,000. After all, you don't rake in that kind of benefit money just by sitting on your backside waiting for people to shower you with cheques. I admit that there is a fair bit of that, but what you mainly have to do is play exhibition matches in the evening and go to a lot of functions which is *very exhausting indeed*. I can assure you that organizing a benefit is no picnic, although there are quite a few barbecue events. The point I'm making is that if I've achieved anything in life, and the best part of a quarter of a million quid isn't too bad, then I owe it all to the wonderful upbringing I received at Number 15 Foundry Lane.

Mum and Dad were always keen on sport but I don't think they especially wanted me to become a cricketer. They never said so, anyway. In fact they said very little to me at all when I was small, apart from 'never be beholden to anyone' and 'clean your room'. We're like that in our family: unde-monstrative, suspicious and very, very tidy. But Mum also had a great sense of humour. I remember when I was first picked for Kirklington Second XI, Mum sent me off with my cricket kit immaculately clean and pressed as ever but she had a funny look in her eye. It wasn't until I took the field that I realized she'd screwed my studs to the inside of my boots. That afternoon was the first of many occasions whereby I bowled with a boot full of blood! I think it was Mum's way of making sure I didn't get above myself. She's still very protective like that. Even now, she'll say to me, 'Don't go getting ideas, David, and you'll never be disappointed.'

Dad (Dave Podmore senior) could be a laugh too, in his own individual way. I remember he took me out into our backyard on the morning of my tenth birthday. There, in front of me, leaning against the coal bunker, was this beautiful, bright-red racing bike; five gears, dynamo, mirrors – the lot. I was about to get on it when Mum and Dad suddenly burst out laughing. They had only borrowed the bike from the shop and the present they had *really* got me was a left-footed roller skate. My face must have been a picture! I can see the funny side now of course, but at the time I wasn't too impressed! The next year Dad bought me another roller skate – a left one again, needless to say. How he chuckled. You can see where I got my love of practical jokes.

As a family, we were never that fussed about holidays but we went anyway, usually to Mablethorpe or Skegness, and it was on the sands of Skeggie and Thorpey that my cricketing character was formed. I learned lessons on those beaches that would last me a lifetime in the game. I shall never forget the Skeggie slope; by God, after running up that for a couple of overs you were praying for rain, I can tell you. Mum always had choice of ends, of course, which was right, and Dad did most of the batting, and I had no complaints about that either. But that wind at Mablethorpe! I'd give it three or four deliveries and if I had no joy I'd conveniently 'pick up a niggle' and retire to the outfield. I always used to try and field by a break-water – that way I could slip off for a pie or a smoke without anyone noticing.

Weather was always a factor at Skeg. There was one year when it absolutely poured down and I don't think we bowled a ball from one Sunday to the next. I still say it's the best holiday I ever had; we spent the whole week playing cards in the digs. That was the year Dad discovered you could get into the Arcadia Theatre for nothing if you waited until the interval. We saw the second half of The Barron Knights' act fourteen times that week. Great days.

Money was always tight, in fact it was often the only thing we ever talked about. And it was money that caused my first brush with authority. I'd been at my junior school for a couple of years and although I wasn't exactly an Einstein scholastically I'd always done what was asked – no more and no less – and I felt that after six terms I deserved a benefit. The headmaster obviously didn't see it that way. He gave me a brown envelope at the end of term and not a penny piece did it contain, just a wad of school reports and some stuff about forthcoming events. I thought that was very disappointing.

I had a similar problem at my next school. It was over a puppet show I was putting on for my classmates (early signs that I would one day spend my winters appearing in pantomime). The headmaster thought I was overcharging, I thought I was worth it and once again there was an acrimonious parting of the waves with the local media typically siding with the establishment.

As I became increasingly saddened by the way I was treated by the powers-that-be, cricket began to play a much bigger part in my life. By the time I was thirteen I'd turned myself into a fairly useful bits-and-pieces player and a lot of the Dave Podmore trademarks were already in place: the gold chains, the grunt in the delivery stride and I had also developed the knack of smearing vital singles in diarrhoea situations. Then out of the blue came my big break. A nationwide chicken-pox epidemic suddenly catapulted me into the frame for the England Under-14s tour of the West Indies.

They talk about the smell of success, this was my first sniff of it and, believe me, it smelt good –

good and ripe anyway, since this was the first occasion I was sharing a dressing-room with Gatt and Beefy. The lads were full of high spirits even in those days. I remember Gower making Goochie cry because he wouldn't let him have a go with his model aeroplane – sadly, we all know what that led to. Lubo was very much the star of the side and even then he knew how to track down a glass of something cold and acceptable. Consequently, our results against the West Indies Under-14s were disappointing. We were skittled out for under 50 in most of our matches by the young Curtly Ambrose. Curtly was only eighteen months old at the time but he was still too quick for most of us. Backed up by poor pitches and biassed umpiring we never really had a price against him. We used to pray for the drinks break when his mum would take him off for a feed.

It was on that tour that I met the girl who was to become my first wife. Toni was a member of the Rothmans Under-14s Personality Girls Squad who were following us round the Caribbean learning their trade just as we lads were. The relationship was doomed from the start. I could tell by the way she used to draw a flower above the 'i' in Toni that she had ideas above her station and things went from bad to worse until the incident which finally destroyed our marriage (see Chapter 13).

It was clear that cricket would be my life but I also applied myself to my studies, somehow managing to scrape through my Intermediary Casino Management Diploma. But my heart was never in academic pursuits. Where I wanted to be was out there on the park putting it there or thereabouts and keeping it cat's-arse tight at the death.

Inevitably, I grew away from the ordinary world of Foundry Lane, but Mum and Dad continued to be important figures in my life. Just before Dad died I remember him digging his bony fingers into my arm and wheezing, 'Never do anyone a good turn, Son, if you can do them a bad one instead.' I've tried to pass on what I learned from Mum and Dad to my own lad (Dave Podmore Junior).

Even though Dad never came to watch me play he was a keen cricket fan and in accordance with his wishes we scattered his ashes over the Nursery End at Lord's on the day before the England v South Africa test of '94. It was a very special and moving moment for me when, on the third day, Mike Atherton suddenly bent down, picked Dad up and put him in his pocket. I couldn't believe my eyes when, half an hour after tea, Athers starts rubbing Dad on to one side of the ball, then he chucks it to Goughie and the next thing I know Dad's being clattered through the covers for four. I think it's what he would have wanted. It certainly would have appealed to his sense of humour.

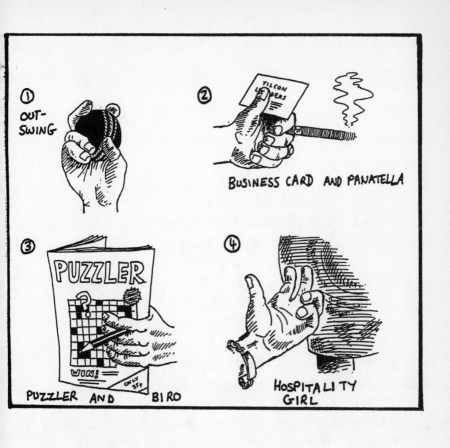

THE GRIP: An omniportant part of the county cricketer's armoury

3

A COMPLETE PRO

Cricket is like life:
You have lunch and tea,
But not breakfast in the case of cricket,
obviously.
And sometimes it rains.

Dave Podmore. Abergavenny, 1992

By the time I was nineteen I had bought my first pair of Alsatian pups. I had spent a winter in South Africa and I had been on the books of three different counties. I knew it all, didn't I? The truth is I knew about as much about being a professional cricketer as Rin-Tin-Tin knows about brain surgery! To give you an idea of how green I was, I had no idea how to order a curry, I'd never bought a copy of *The Puzzler* and I hadn't even *heard* of Len Deighton. And I called myself a professional cricketer!

It was a big stroke of luck that I came into the Derbyshire dressing-room in the twilight years of one of the greatest craftsmen the game has ever known, Ted Crapp. Ted took me under his wing that first season and the wisdom he passed on to me as we drove from ground to ground in his old red and white Hillman Imp – well, you can forget Oxford and Cambridge, quite honestly. Ted would talk for hours on end about his misfortunes and grievances, pausing only for me to slot another lighted Capstan between his emaciated lips. I've never heard a man cough like Ted – one spasm sent us spinning off the Nuneaton by-pass and straight into the bottom of a ditch. If Fred Swarbrook hadn't been following behind on his Matchless I think Ted would still be there now cursing, with his foot hard down and the engine in reverse. I don't know how we managed to squeeze Ted into Fred's side-car. Laugh? You could have strolled up my arse with an armful of cane furniture!

I idolised Ted. I would try to model my game on his, bowling the ball that little bit slower and flatter or taking that extra half hour to score my first run. I once deliberately ran myself out at the end of a Sunday league game just so he'd be home in time for the Black and White Minstrel Show. But he never thanked me, he just borrowed my towel and told me to fetch him a Mackeson as usual.

Gradually I began to fit into the side and although I didn't take that many wickets – couple of two-fors in the Championship and the occasional tidy none-for in the Benson's – all the time I was learning the game from the inside. I was picking up those tricks of the trade that go unnoticed by most of our faithful supporters – even the ones who have special plastic sheets to keep their scorebooks dry.

When I read all this stuff being dished up by our beloved media on the subject of ball-tampering, I can't resist observing, somewhat sardonically perhaps, 'Blimey, anyone would think it's something new.' Ask any of the older players and they'll tell you Douglas Jardine used to buy his bottle-tops by the hundredweight. Wally Hammond's pockets were so full of resin he could hardly stand up. C. B. Fry? Thumbnails like flaming Segovia. You knew where you stood with men like that, whereas with these Pakistanis you never know what they'll get up to. It's a bloody disgrace.

Naturally it was dear old Ted who first showed me how to 'look after the ball'. They talk about players having flair, well Ted had flares, and big ones too. They were so wide at the bottom he could carry a Black and Decker strapped to his calf. As soon as the ball stopped swinging Ted would whip out a screwdriver and change the sanding disc without the umpire noticing a thing – and this was long before the introduction of the cordless drill. What an artist! Now, of course, he is known to thousands of cricket fans as the most efficient gateman on the county circuit.

In those days 'sponsorship' was one of those words I had heard floating around the dressing-room, and, like 'ubiquitous', I'd never bothered to find out what it meant. But it became abundantly clear at the end of that first Derbyshire season when I met a certain gentleman who was to become the most important influence on my life. He was best man at my second wedding and has promised to do it again at my third, we've been friends for over twenty years and his name is of course Ray Poole. Ray is now one of the most successful entrepreneurs in the East Midlands, what with the area Nissan concession and fingers in just about every pie in Hinckley. But in those days he was just another jug-eared sales rep working for Value Petfoods UK of Uttoxeter. He was an ambitious so-and-so like me and one evening at the Fiesta Club in Matlock he laid a proposition before me. Would I be interested in a sponsorship arrangement with Value Petfoods? A tin of dog food for every wicket I took for Derbyshire? Would I ever? It was no picnic feeding two Alsatian pups on a junior pro's wages, I nearly bit his hand off.

In fact I just shook it and that was it. Nothing on paper, no contract, we simply trusted each other. That's the way it's been for the last twenty years and we've not had one cross word (apart from on the driving range when he cracks on that he's hit the 200-yard spot while I wasn't looking!). What I didn't know at the time was that Ray had no authorisation from Ian Brain, the head honcho at Value Petfoods UK, and he was therefore taking a huge flyer. Not only did Ray secure the dog food sponsorship for me but, by the end of the season, he'd tied up an Odour-Eaters endorsement and done a publishing deal for my first book, *AY-UP, I'VE PISSED MISSEN! – 500 of the Best Derbyshire Cricketing Anecdotes!*. He's one in a million is Ray.

They viewed me with a bit more respect in the dressing-room after this. It was a big moment for me when I came in to find eleven tins of dog food stacked on top of my locker. There was something in Ted Crapp's expression as he applied his medication which said, 'All right, lad. Tha'll do.' I knew I had arrived.

POD IN PEWTER

PODDINGTON BEAR
(BAT, PADS, CAP & BALL
NOT INCLUDED)

WILLIE WICKETZ (uses household tap water)

The Pod Collection
Better-than-average merchandising to cherish.

4

RAIN STARTS PLAY

In the springtime of the year when the grounds-man's mower chugs across the square and crick-eters begin to thread their way around the M25, there is an unmistakeable, early-season freshness in the air; it's called April Freshness and it's one of an exciting new range of car air-fresheners which I am happy to be endorsing throughout the coming season.

In-car fragrance is just one of the thousand-and-one things the pro has to think of before embark-ing on the six gruelling months of an English county season. Over the years Dave Podmore has become a massive repository of such nuggets of cricketing wisdom and these days I am con-stantly being asked, 'Come on Pod, share some of that knowledge around, you mean bastard.' Fair enough. Here then is Dave Podmore's guide to survival in the fast lane of English county cricket.

NICKNAMES

Next to a car, a nickname is probably the most important piece of professional equipment a cricketer needs. You can spend all the time in the world in the nets or on the 'stair-master' but if you haven't got a nickname then I hope you like orange squash because you're going to be carrying a good few trays of it.

Every schoolboy dreams of walking out to bat at Lord's with a nickname like Goochie or Stewie or Gatt but unfortunately nicknames that ooze that kind of class don't come along that often. They have to be worked at.

I'll give you an example. A few years ago, Robin Smith was one of eighteen 'Smithies' on the circuit. Useful, but nothing to write home about. So he went back to the drawing board, worked hard through the winter of '88 and came out on the park next April as 'The Judge'. Two months later he's 'Judgey' and by the end of the year he was dispatching the Windies to all parts. At the time of writing he's busy taming the Bok.

Nowhere has the importance of nicknames been more starkly demonstrated than in the unfortunate case of Durham. There were times last summer when they were struggling to put eleven nicknames on the field. I've offered to take the lads off to Antigua for a couple of weeks next March and hopefully we will be able to put a few things right. I am confident that by next August a lot of the younger Durham boys will be knocking on the nickname door.

The fact that I currently hold the record for the number of nicknames in a career (see Statistics section) is all very nice for the ego et cetera but, to be honest, it has become a bit of an albatross (which is Craig White's nickname, I believe). I can't wait for the day when some young lad breaks away from the pack and smashes the ten-nickname barrier. Once it happens, mark my words, you will see double-figure nicknames as a matter of course. There is a promising lad at Leicester called 'Spoonhead' who I have my eye on. He is also called Prickdust, Bungalow-bollocks, Chutney Man, Hector's House and Deltoid Fartboy but he's definitely one for your notebooks.

DIET

As a top athlete you simply can't afford not to respect your body. I'm something of a health freak, as any of the lads will tell you, and it's quite common for me to completely purge my system before and after a big game. A prawn madras or mutton vindaloo normally does the trick. Personally, I've yet to taste a curry that's too hot, but it *is* important to exercise a bit of caution with the so-called Ring-sting Diet. Even in my neck of the woods (the East Midlands), by no means every Balti house and Tandoori Centre is 'trundler friendly', as my old *compadres* 'Spamhead' and 'Urine Man' will ruefully testify. Thank God for the Brumbrella!

I think I may have already mentioned that fizzy drinks tend to blow me up and after a hard game I prefer to take something non-gassy. I'm afraid all those pictures you've seen of Pod toasting victory on the players' balcony are a bit of a cheat. It's not champagne you can see in my glass at all. It's Drambuie. Drambuie is an ancient Scottish drink and I first discovered that it agreed with me on Ray and Jean Poole's anniversary at the Moat House. As long as you clean your teeth before going to sleep there are no disagreeable after-effects. I would be more than happy to meet with any representatives of the Drambuie organisation as I believe the East Midlands is a sitting target.

SMOKING

Another area where I'm a bit of a stickler. I absolutely hate cigarettes. If I've run out of pana-tellas I will occasionally have one of Spamhead's Superkings but I don't enjoy it. I did try a pipe for a while in the seventies and I've flirted with Camels, but the truth is I'm a panatella man through and through. And I really do mean 'through and through' because a panatella will get things moving of a morning quicker than any amount of stoned fruit and black coffee. It is fair to say that, around the county dressing-rooms, my quarter-to-eleven whiff is among the best-known features of the summer. The umpires often time their walk to the middle by my regular morning ritual. The fact is that during the pre-lunch session I'm more comfortable in the field than some players half my age. As I'm forever telling the lads I coach at the Dave Podmore Academy, cricket is all about gaining the advantage.

TRAINING

Have you noticed the amount of rubbish spouted by so-called fitness experts these days? I have. You can do all the press-ups and stomach-crunches you like but what good is it if you can't put it there or thereabouts? What use is a fast-twitch fibre when you're trying to keep it cat's-arse tight at the death? And can someone please explain to me how a five-mile run helps you smear a priceless single in a diarrhoea finish?

The truth is that the athlete has to tailor his training programme to his individual needs. For instance, when I'm bowling in a match I tend to go fairly red in the face and puff my cheeks out. It might not suit everybody but it's the right method for me – so round about the end of March I begin some very gentle face-flexing exercises and gradually incorporate them into my grunt co-ordination routine. April, I work on bending down and adjusting my knee support (something I like to do at least twice before every delivery in a match situation). May/June, I practise shouting 'Catch it!', then putting my hands on my hips and going 'F*ck's sake'. I reckon to be fit by about mid-July. This is an absolutely critical stage of the season if your side is still in the hunt for honours. If it isn't you'll be in the Costcutter Cup where, as we know, there are ladders to be won.

ALWAYS LOOK NEAT
AND DO YOURSELF JUSTICE

Has been my motto for twenty-three seasons and it hasn't exactly let me down, has it? I suppose I learned most of what I know about looking good in the seventies. Trouser bottoms may narrow and widen but neatness never goes out of fashion. Like all senior players I spend a good deal of time on corporate outreach. I might have to go from a meeting of my benefit committee (at the Moat House's superbly appointed Tilehurst suite) to a brainstorming session with Ray Poole in the Dyno-Rod tent. With a schedule like mine you can't afford not to take a pride in your appearance.

Sky-blue slacks, fawn blazer and grey slip-ons get me where I need to go. Clark's do an Active-Air shoe now with parallel lines of stitching and a velcro fastener which combines comfort with style. Slacks though are the clincher.

Ray Poole and I are currently in negotiations with Austin Reed over our design for a new executive slack which has a handful of loose change already sewn into the pocket, so you've always got something to jingle while networking in the hospitality tents. We all know that awful moment when, right in the middle of forging a corporate contact, you slide your hand into your pocket only to find you're jingling thin air like a complete idiot. Hopefully Podslax will make 'no-change nightmare' a thing of the past.

Since hospitality-tent networking is a by no means un-convivial activity involving fairly regular trundles to and from the Portaloo, and since Podslax are a slim-fitting trouser specially designed to show off the contours of the wearer's physique, there is a slight risk of tell-tale-executive-damp-patch in the groin area. But we've overcome this problem completely. Each pair of Podslax comes with a complimentary tube of

'Pissex' which is a viscous fluid exactly matching the colour of the trouser material. You apply it with a brush to the affected area as you leave the Portaloo – and return to the hospitality tent with complete confidence.

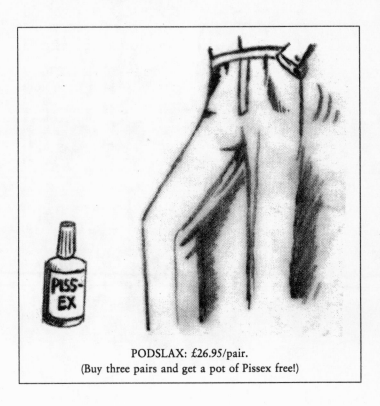

PODSLAX: £26.95/pair.
(Buy three pairs and get a pot of Pissex free!)

THE DAVE PODMORE MASTERCLASS

5

CHARITY BEGINS AT HOVE

Nothing gives me a bigger kick than doing a bit for sick kiddies and having a bloody good laugh while I'm about it. I play a lot of cricket for the Lord's Taverners and, boy oh boy, do we have a whole heap of fun. When you've got guys like Roger de Courcy and Javed Miandad acting the giddy goat – add a pinch of Keith Harris and Orville and you've got a recipe for total mayhem. Laugh? Imagine sitting in the Palladium for seven and a half hours on a hot Sunday afternoon and you won't be far off!

As well as being helpless with laughter most of the time we also play some damn good cricket. I generally open the bowling either with Michael Fish or Lord Soper. I move it away, Fishy and Sopes nip it back. Su Pollard keeps it there or thereabouts, although she's mainly there to provide the concrete in the middle order. Oliver Reed hits the deck fairly hard. Tony Slattery gives it a big rip out the back of the hand, and as for Keith Harris, well, he can make that ball talk – literally!

We had a great game at Hove last year. An absolutely perfect day, only slightly marred by an incident which I'll tell you about because I ended up taking a not inconsiderable quantity of stick for it – unfairly in my opinion, but judge for yourself.

It happened like this. Our skipper, Cardinal Basil Hume, won the toss and inserted. He chucks me the cherry saying, 'God be with you, my son' – *or words to that effect*!!! I look down the other end of the track to see that, opening the batting for the Celebrity XI is the very lovely Selina Scott. Now, I've always believed that this game is about taking your chances when you get them because, believe me, they don't come that often (I'm sure Selina would say the same about newscasting). So I gave her a couple of quickish bouncers and a head-high snot-boxer just to test her out and generally let her know I was on the park.

Now, I want there to be absolutely no doubt about this – *no one was more concerned than me when Selina hit the deck* (although of course I couldn't show it because that would have meant relinquishing the psychological ascendancy which I'd worked so hard to secure). Granted, there was a fair bit of blood and perhaps another time I wouldn't point her towards the pavilion with quite such an emphatic gesture, but, even so, the reaction of the players and crowd seemed totally out of proportion. The way I see it, there was no way you could call Selina a tail-ender batting that high up the order. Besides, nobody clatters Pod for two fours in a row like that and gets away with it. The important thing though, was that Selina and I were able to have a beer and a good laugh about it in the hospital afterwards. End of story.

How The Nation's Cartoonists Saw
The Selina Scott Incident

Daily Telegraph
(Search me what this one's about. It just goes to show that
you should keep sport out of politics)

" *I WOULDN'T MIND BEING HIT IN THE FACE BY ONE OF HER BOUNCERS!*"

The Sun
(That's more like it. Great laugh).

35

Evening Standard
(Ouch: Having a laugh and keeping the sponsors happy –
that's what the game is all about).

BRINGING KIDDIES OUT OF COMAS

This is definitely the most rewarding of all my charity activities. I have had no medical training whatsoever and yet I seem to have this knack, call it a gift, of coaxing a kiddy back from the brink of oblivion. All I do is sit on the edge of the bed, blow a little panatella smoke under their noses, then whisper in their tiny ears about all the good things they are missing as a result of being in a coma: watching their hero smear a winning single in the Costcutter Cup, that sort of thing. Then I play them a tape of some of the highlights of my career: the '37' at Worksop, a couple of diarrhoea finishes and selected extracts from my *Diary of a Tour*, read by Robin Askwith of *Confessions of a Window Cleaner* fame.

Nine times out of ten we get a result. Their little eyelids flicker and I tiptoe from the room. Job done. No fuss.

If I am in the middle of a benefit year however, my busy schedule sometimes prevents me from visiting the hospital. I might have a clutch and brake centre to open for example or I might have to attend a fund-raising potato-pie supper. If I can't get to the kiddy, I find that a clear, crisp 'Come On! Wake Up!!' down the mobile will often do the trick. *And* it saves me the petrol to the hospital (which parents never offer to refund funnily enough).

TRANSCRIPT OF DAVE PODMORE'S POPULAR AFTER-DINNER SPEECH

The Moathouse
Oadby

Good evening gentlemen or should I say ███████
There were these two Pakistanis. One says ██████
████████ building site ████████ gorilla █████
lips ███████ jumbo-jets ██████ mothercare ██
██████ pearly gates ████████ four of his mates
come through the door saying 'our turn now
please Sahib' ████████████████████████████████
██

████ Don't get me wrong but ██████████████████
██

Madras ████████████████████████████ I've got
nothing against ████████ hey, man █████ jungle
████████████████████ bicycle ██████████████
Samantha Fox ████████████████████ a week to clear
it up ████████████████ the third giraffe says never
mind the slug pellets, where's the ████████ cheese
gone? Right, any questions?

I don't know about that but there were these two

Indian waiters walking down the street. One says ██

██

I don't know about that but I'll tell you what, if Ray Illingworth had his ██████████████ and his ██

██

███████████ he'd be getting off lightly. Thank you very much ladies and gentlemen, God bless, safe journey home and if you're driving, make sure you've got a ████████████████ car.

6

MUSINGS FROM THE BOUNDARY ROPE

People think all fielding in the deep means is you have time to take a nice leisurely swig of your Isotonic drink placed just inside the boundary. Not a bit of it. I have a strict code of behaviour when I'm put out there. I'm not talking about the fatuous law from HQ that says it's an automatic four if the ball hits the bottle before crossing the rope. All I'd say to that is – what if it rebounds off the bottle, shoots up the field and hits a helmet stored behind the sticks? I suppose you get NINE for that!

And, come to think of it, a close look at the scorebook for Mister Lara's so-called 500-odd not out may reveal that it wasn't such a towering achievement after all due to a couple of dozen or so such flukes. Study the video and count the bottles round the boundary first before going overboard with the brown-nosing praise, I say.

No, I like to let my mind roam through the lush green outfield of the history of this game of ours. I don't just mean the 1950s or the pre-war period or even the Victorian era, I'm talking about the twelfth century – BC! In those days (and nobody realises this) they played the game with a pig's stomach and a bat called a 'crugg'. I can't remember what the stumps were called or what they did about leg-byes, but Ralph Dellor has all the details. The point is that cricket is very, very old. So don't tell me there's anything new about it because it bloody well isn't!

Now, I don't want to be one of those sad characters with car-rugs over their windscreens who are forever going on about the old days, but I wouldn't mind a little bet that Lumpy Stevens would have sorted out friend Lara in a couple of overs, no problem. Lord Frederick Beauclerk? He'd have clattered Shane Warne all over the park. Badminton Park, it probably would have been. And he'd still have time to shoot a brace of good fat pheasant before joining the ladies for whist and witty conversation.

I mean, be honest, who can say whether Bradman was better than Andy Moles? And it's hard to believe he could eat more boiled eggs at a sitting than Flat Jack Simmons. Try telling a Northants fan that Lord Hawke could light his farts further than David Capel – and then retire several paces!

41

All you can ever be sure of is that they were the best of their time.

Call me a silly Pod if you like, but I'm also partial, when walking in small circles placing one boot in front of the other, to conducting one-on-one imaginary conversations with some of my heroes from the past, genuine great names from cricket's Hall of Fame who, like me I tend to find, didn't have it easy. Time-travelling in Pod's mental Tardis can turn up some facts which may surprise you. Dennis Compton, to give you a for-instance, vouchsafed me the *real* story behind that famous partnership between him and Bill Edrich when they won the Ashes for us in 1950-odd at the Oval.

The all-mouth-and-no-trousers brigade at Wisdens Almanack will tell you that Dennis turned to Bill and said, 'We'd better get them in singles, agreed, Edrich?' 'Agreed, Compton,' came back the reply, the two of them both being Professionals and therefore forced by the powers-that-be to address each other thus (not to mention having to dubbin P. B. H. May's boots and park their bikes round the side of the tube station). In actual fact Bill thought that Dennis said, 'We'd better get them *in* in singles', and came to the conclusion that the bar was about to shut and they ought to get a move on before it was 'Time Gentlemen and Players Please'. Result: Dennis and Bill staggered on to the field in a state of less than total ebriation!

As Dennis himself put it to me, 'I don't mind telling you, Pod – I was so p****d I thought I was batting with a runner!'

Some pretty interesting information comes my way too, when I'm free-associating out there in the country. Prince Ranjitsinhji it was who reminisced about taking the other England lads – Hobbsy, C. B. Fry-y – out for a post-match curry in the '20s. Where we'd say 'Who fancies a Ruby?' or 'How about a Pete?', apparently the correct terminology in that era was 'Anyone for an Arthur?', after the Arthur Murray School of Dancing!

Incidentally, Ranji-y went on to add that in the restaurant it was the waiters who called *him* 'Gunga Din' and not the other way round as per now . . . and what's more he DIDN'T MIND A BIT. Try telling that to some of the sensitive souls who are taking all the affectionate rough-and-tumble out of cricket, running off to the Law Courts in floods of tears at every opportunity! To my mind the game's been changing a lot lately, and not for the better. Which is what I found myself saying to the legendary W. G. Grace one afternoon last season, when I'd been put behind the tree at Canterbury. The fat ranged far and wide as we chewed it, and while I can't claim we put the world to rights, we made a fair stab at improving that part of it that has deck-chairs and cool boxes round the edges!

'Settle an argument, Gracey,' I began. 'You're a fully paid-up member of the Beardies' Union – what do you reckon to *my* face-fuzz? Should I let it grow all season, or just for the duration of a match, like Goochie . . . who then has it shaved off and transplanted into his scalp?'

'Good question, Pod,' came back the Great Man. 'What a lot of people haven't cottoned on to about my beard is that it's perfect for having a go at the ball with. I crack on I'm lovably twinkling my eyes and scratching my chin, whereas what's really happening is, I'm hiding the cherry in there and moving it about in the undergrowth until the seam is well and truly lifted!'

Pod: Top wheeze. But what if the umpire spotted you doing it, and accused you of cheating? You've got a lot to lose, being like me something of a living legend.

Grace: I'd have no alternative but to punch his lights out. And as a doctor of course, I could attend to him then and there on the pitch, and charge the guy for the privilege! Don't forget, Pod, it's me the crowd's paid to come and see, not those bastards in white coats. That's why they double the price of admission when I'm playing.

Pod: The lads in the dressing room say the crowd should get twice their money back when *I* turn out!

Grace: Yeah? Just point to that sponsored brougham of yours in the cart park, see who's laughing then! You're the backbone of this funny old game, Pod – don't let anybody tell you any different.

Pod: Fair comment.

Grace: I mean, sure – I can go out there, score 2,000 runs and take 200 wickets in 1895. But look at it this way – nobody likes a smart aleck!

Pod: Mega-achievement, Gracey, nevertheless.

Grace: Don't get me wrong. You've got to give Jack his jerkin. But there's another side to it, ain't there? Most of that season I was well brassed off because there was a new Sherlock Holmes sitting waiting for me in the pav, and *could* I get into it? Then my brother Ted reads it first and tells me the ending while we're at third slip and gully. Thanks a lot, Our Kid!

Pod: Who are your own heroes in history, Gracey?

Grace: King Canute, without a shadow. He backed himself against the elements and refused to listen to the doom-and-gloom merchants. Didn't come off on the day, but he gave it 450%.

Pod: So, by the same token you think I should ignore all those people who say I should retire and get a job outside the game? They run into several hundred now, from all walks of life.

Grace: Listen to your inner voices. They'll tell you when it's time to quit.

Pod: Thanks for the prescription, Doc!

Grace: Don't mention it. Now here's one for *you*, Pod – would you say the glare of the media spotlight is worse than when I played the game?

Pod: Very much so. There's nothing the media likes better than to build a man up and then grind him into the mud like an old rag.

Grace: Sounds like you're talking from bitter experience, my young friend!

Pod: Oh, you know. Talking of giving 450%, did I ever tell you about the day in 1983 I was having a toad* on a real bunsen* . . . at Grace Road, oddly enough? Talk about laugh! It was just after tea, and . . .

Grace: Aye aye, here comes the Barmy Army – just back from trouncing the Zulus by the look of it. Sorry Pod, better go. Another time.

Pod: Nice talking to you anyway, Gracey!

And we go our separate ways, into the setting sun.

* 'Toad' – toad in the hole = bowl
* 'Bunsen' – bunsen burner = turner

THE DAVE PODMORE MASTERCLASS

7

TOWARDS FUTURE TOMORROWS:

Dave Podmore's Guide to Better Management

Many's the time some fresh-faced young shaver's come down to my end of the track as the two of us approached Brown Trouser Time towards the end of a run chase, and said, 'Pod, what would *you* do in my situation? Would you put your money into PEPs or let your manager invest it in a new range of drive-thru tapas bars?' It's a matter of some pride to me that my business acumen is considered by thinkers in the game to be on the same par as my bowling: occasionally expensive but always reluctant to give anything away.

So when Ray Poole approached me with the idea of starting up my own Man-Management course I gave it careful consideration. I have to say I'd always had deep pity for the white-collar worker, turning up at the same place day after day, year in year out, achieving very little and with nothing to show for it except frustration as he went for a consoling beer with his colleagues each evening.

And up to then my idea of a 'Learning Curve' had been the tradition we had at Derbyshire of starting a new season by finding out who could p*** highest out of the dressing-room lav window! This provided no little amount of innocent fun and laughter . . . and dampness for all concerned when it was the turn of a certain fast bowler whose name is not unadjacent to Cornwall, with his much-envied ability to spray it everywhere!

But Ray convinced me that there might be something in this Motivation lark, after showing me a book on the same subject written by Will Carling. Time to even up the score with that particular gentleman I thought: we've always had a bit of a love-hate relationship, ever since Jacqui and I were pipped at the post by Mr and Mrs C for a lucrative contract to advertise a low-fat savoury bake. All I'll say on that matter is: who's still popping her fella's dinner in the micro-wave, Julia or Jacqui?

I also recollect the day I received my benefit cheque from the East Midlands Area Manager of British Gas (as it was then) for services rendered in my second spell playing for Leicestershire. He was a speckle-faced, ginger-haired lad who was much impressed by the size of the cheque (and not simply because it measured four feet by two feet!) He asked me my secret, to which I gave my usual reply: 'Whoever said small is beautiful is talking spherical objects in the approximate vicinity of the groin region!' That young man's name was Cedric Brown, and I hear he's been getting some attention as one of the highest scorers in the Privatised Utilities XI!

In other words, Pod was at the cutting edge all the time without realising it and, since that Champagne Road to Damascus Moment, I've been doing my bit towards keeping Great Britain plc in the game through my series of Sport/Management Interface Seminars held at Moat Houses up and down the country around Hinckley. My ability to maximise my potential – off the park as well as on – has served as an inspiration to countless lower-order middle-managers who have attended my 'Podivation' lectures . . . motivation with added D.V.P.!

Because what Ray Poole and I have done, successfully, is taken what I said to the gasman, bottled it and put it on a shelf marked 'Danger. Strong Stuff.' What each delegate gets for his or her £250 per head (plus VAT; coffee and Moat House Biscuit Barrel Selection not included) is pure, unadulterated liquid Pod of the kind that would carry a Government Health Warning if it weren't so good for you!

WIN

My message to the Skippers of Tomorrow is summed up by this acronym. Quite simply it stands for 'Winning Is Not-as-good-as-putting-it-there-or-thereabouts'. Talent really is no substitute for sheer hard call-me-old-fashioned graft. The distinctive bouquet of sweat mixed with elbow grease coming from the Chardonnay Room at the end of a day's seminar sums up exactly what I try to get across. It's all very well achieving honours and putting silver on your sideboard – anyone can do that, as Dermot Reeve has proved time and again. No, the real challenge is to get out there and do the job, result or no result. The sort of show-offs who continually appear on Sports Personality of the Year and get to call Stephen Hendry and Fatima Whitebread 'Steve' and 'Fat' – these are often the most hated and despised members of the dressing-room, leading to an atmosphere of division and tension, and the use of their kit bag as a toilet.

A

Another seminal buzz-word on my flip-chart is A. 'A' stands for 'Application' – something which will be found engraved on my heart the day I die (alongside Oadby Vintners, Ray Poole Motors and any other currently paid-up sponsors, obviously).

Application is the key to doing yourself justice. To illustrate this, delegates are shown a short piece of film of a test match at Lord's. The Mound Stand is empty as all the complimentary ticket-holders have gone off for lunch in a hospitality tent. We see them rolling back shortly after the tea interval. It's a sickening sight and I give top marks to the first delegate who jumps up and shouts, 'What the heck do they think they're doing – coming back this early?'

Exactly! Why do they think they're there? *To do some serious Networking, of course!* What's the point of wasting valuable S.T. (Schmoozing Time) watching cricket till stumps when they should be conquering the world to which that ticket is a passport; of World Class flesh-pumping, business-card-swapping, mobile phone-call making and car-key twirling?

In other words, putting it in language we can all chant:

NO APPLICATION = NO CONTACTS = NO CAREER PROSPECTS = NO WAY FORWARD, JOSE! (OR 'COLIN', MORE PROBABLY).

Now, in case anyone has difficulty remembering these handy acronyms, I've devised another, to remind them how important acronyms are in management thinking: this is quite simply

ACRONYM

Which stands for 'Acronyms Can Really Optimise Now Your Message'. The sticklers for detail among you may notice that it should really read 'Acronyms Can Really Optimise Your Message Now' – but that would spell ACROYMN, which looks about as peculiar and unbalanced as Craig White coming in fifth-wicket down instead of at Number Eleven (!!).

Fig. 1

Step aside 'e = mcc²'! This simple formula has motivated under-achievers everywhere.

But there's more to Podivation than the words 'WIN', 'A' and 'ACRONYM' flashing up on the overhead projector. The superb, value-for-money package also includes Interactive Team-Building, Role-Play and not a few diagrams. Here's how it works. Once we've got the chaps and chap-esses together, and I've relaxed them with one or two good stories about the times I've been caught in the nude in that particular hotel (for full gory details see the 'Podders Starkers!' chapter) we get down to the deadly serious business of creating highly motivated groups that are both hungry and thirsty. That's when they find out that refreshments aren't included in the overall package – where-upon I allow half an hour for a demonstration of Survival Skills, when groups are encouraged to roam the corridors looking for the packets of sugar and pats of butter left on trays outside room doors. Then I split them into teams: if it's an Allied Carpets workshop it might be Wilton versus Axminster, or, if I'm in a good mood, the 70/30 Wool Acrylic Supertwist lads up against the Foam-backed Double Fleck Berberites (for areas of Heavy Domestic Use). Then we play cricket.

Obviously, we can't *literally* play cricket, at any rate not the hard-core stuff you get at Fenners in April. Moat House Banqueting Suites are, for the most part, surprisingly ill-equipped to double up as first-class venues, with no short boundaries and no uneven bounce due to the parquet dance-floor, though they have made a start with the giant TV screens. And, with Pod steaming in towards you from the Creche End, it's not long before you're caught up in the virtual reality of the game, forging Team Spirit by absorbing cricket's finer aspects, such as:

A) IDENTIFYING THE WEAKEST MEMBER OF THE TEAM AND TAKING THE PISS OUT OF THEM

It might be a bald git, or a fat bloke, or a woman who's never so much as picked up a ball, gobbed on it and rubbed it up and down in her crotch before. Either way a good dose of mockery and abuse such as:

SLAPHEAD
LARD PANTS
STUPID TART

soon has the rest of the team pulling together and acting in unison with enormous benefits for morale, which will no doubt be reflected in the next month's sales sheets!

B) LARKING ABOUT

Hiding shoes, throwing rolled-up pieces of toilet paper at each other (used/unused as preferred), pulling chairs away just as someone's about to sit down, condom in the water-cooler . . . all these tried-and-tested Britannic Assurance County Championship dressing-room practices are easily transposed into a High Street or Shopping Mall environment, and can greatly reduce the tedium of dealing with customers' carpeting requisites.

C) ACCEPTING RESPONSIBILITY

Never be afraid to take personal responsibility for pointing the finger. If you don't do it, someone else will, and you'll get the blame for the team's failure to beat Cumberland in the First Round of the Nat West (when in fact it was Rodney Ontong who didn't make his ground in time for a clear-cut single, due in no small part to his wearing a joke plastic bottom).

Is it any wonder that everyone who's attended my seminars comes out literally speechless? With these Life Lessons on board, and hopefully no bones broken, potential Captains of Industry are now super-equipped for getting a result. They also get to go home with a certificate signed by me, a

sponsorship form for *them* to sign and a complimentary Ray Poole Motors torch-pen. And, more
than likely, a better than 10% chance of the biggest
prize of all – a trip to Business's equivalent of a
night out at Mr Bojangles . . . an investiture at
Buckingham Palace!

THE DAVE PODMORE MASTERCLASS

8

POD GETS THE NOD

As I say, your ultimate goal as a player has always got to be to get The Nod to get out on the park and go and do a job for your country. I don't think there's any doubt that the most traditional country you can get out on the park and go and do a job for has got to be England. Put it this way, if pulling on the three little lions doesn't give you a very big red, white and blue lump in your throat, then either you're sick in the head or born abroad. Either way, I'd have very little time for you.

That's probably a very old-fashioned view, but I'm afraid I happen to be proud of my heritage. I've got a lot of time for those great, old-fashioned, English values that some fashionable people seem to be in the business of knocking these days. The lads tell me that even my jock-rot smells of traditional British Stilton! But enough of politics. Suffice it to say that, in my book, there is no greater accolade a sportsman can achieve than getting The Nod to pull on the sweater which bears those three little lions. Or just a single lion in the case of a one-day international. Obviously, if it was a day/night floodlit affair you wouldn't have any lions as such and it would be a blue track-suit not a sweater that you'd be looking to pull on, plus you'd have a tin of blue paint to do your pads and gloves. But, either way, it's the ultimate honour and anyone who takes it for granted ought to look for another profession – the media perhaps? (It's just about cynical enough!)

'When did you first get a sniff of The Nod, Pod?' is a question I'm often asked at my no-holds-barred, after-dinner question and answer sessions. The answer is that, like everything else in my life, it's a long story and also a very unfair one. I reckon I've been there or thereabouts for a Nod ever since I was an apprehensive débutant. First there was my fairytale week at Worksop – when we got the better of three diarrhoea finishes on the trot. I felt I had to be in with at least a shout for a sniff of The Nod but, for all the notice the selectors took, I might as well have been parading my credentials on the planet Mars.

Then there was my *annus mirabilis* trot in 1981; I went into the bank holiday weekend just about as adjacent to a Nod as you can get, only to have my hopes dashed when Norman Gifford broke my arm as I tried to smear him at the death on a surface of indifferent bounce. Before I knew it, the Geoff Millers and the Capels and the Chris Cowdreys and the Ian Greigs had blossomed into world-class bits-and-pieces stop-gaps and it looked as though I was never to peddle my wares on the larger stage.

Fair enough. I got my head down and gave 110% for whichever county I happened to be representing at the time. I certainly wasn't going to mope around complaining that Capel couldn't bowl a hoop down Kettering High Street or that I'd visited kiddies in hospital with fewer disabilities than Chris Cowdrey. No, moaning's just not my style.

But what *did* annoy me was the underhand way my non-selection was handled; no phone call, no letter. They couldn't have picked a better way of upsetting my poor sick mother if they'd tried. Sadly, there are some very sick, small-minded people running this game who have only ever wanted one thing, and that thing, I'm sorry to say, is a situation whereby they've got my head on a plate. What a sad reflection that is.

But, as I say, there's no point in grumbling, so at the end of the '91 season I said to myself, 'If you're not appreciated in the country of your birth, Pod, then you might as well take yourself off somewhere where you are' (appreciated that is).

I came very close to going to South Africa. I'd had a very good offer to go back and coach at the

Pochefstroom Reserved-Entry Country Club. I'd
had a lifelong love affair with the veldt. But at the
start of the '90s there were a lot of political
ramifications going on in South Africa which
frankly made the place a lot less attractive to
me, so I decided under the circumstances I
couldn't accept the offer. It meant that, career-
wise, I was more or less staring down both barrels
of a bottomless doldrum. It was very worrying for
both myself and my then-wife, Nikki. Thank you
so very much Mr Mandela.

Consequently, the invitation to go to Cambodia
and play in Pol Pot's new limited overs league
couldn't have come at a better time. Quite a few
English players had turned down the opportunity
to skipper the Khmer Rouge boys because of their
so-called 'political convictions'. I thought that was
a very blinkered attitude. Rather than simply
believe what one read in the media (always a
somewhat risky policy!), I preferred to go to
Cambodia and see for myself. Moreover, I had a
wife and, at that stage, three dogs to support.

Obviously, they had one or two domestic niggles
to sort out but the country also had a hell of a lot
going for it and the way of life appealed very
strongly indeed to both Nikki and myself.

As for Pol Pot (or 'Potters' as I immediately
dubbed him), he was one of the nicest guys you
could ever hope to meet. He was surprisingly

knowledgeable about cricket and had some very interesting ideas about how to deal with slow over rates. Politically, I'd put Potters somewhere to the left of Johnners.

So, there I was relaxing in the hotel bar in Phnom Penh one afternoon, a hollowed-out monkey's skull of something acceptable in my hand, when, all of a sudden, Nikki comes clattering down from the room in a state of not inconsiderable agitation.

'It's that Dexter on the phone, Pod,' she said, adjusting the seat of her bathing costume in the way she always did when she was worked up. 'I think it's The Nod.'

I was so flabbergasted I don't know how I managed to stay upright. The funny thing was that, as we left the bar, it was Nikki who fell flat on her face. She'd got her ankle chain caught in one of the bows at the back of her white stilettos and I had to leave her spark out on the marble floor while I legged it to the reception phone.

Well, Nikki was right. It was Mr Dexter. He was good enough to inform me that the England tour of India had run into a crisis before it had even started and I was to get on a plane and join the squad immediately. Apparently, six of the England party had gone down with dysentery while checking in at the Air India desk at Heathrow. The culprit was thought to be a dodgy luggage trolley, but I'm afraid I didn't give a damn about the whys and wherefores. All that mattered to me was that, at last, I had a genuine chance of a half-decent shout for a shot at a sniff of a pop at a Nod.

And so ended the chapter in my life entitled 'Cambodia', or Kampuchea as Potters insisted we call it. Ahead of me lay the stiffest challenge yet to my bits-and-pieces skills (not to mention my digestive system!!!) – the 1991/92 England Tour of India and Sri Lanka. After eighteen and a half years in the game – and god knows how many sniffs – I would at last be walking into an England dressing-room to find that one of those sniffs had become a reality.

9

DIARRHOEA OF A TOUR: POD AMONG THE RUNS*

24 October
Day one.

I know everybody says this but as we drove along in the air-conditioned comfort of the coach, the squalor, the smell and the sheer degradation of the people came as a tremendous shock to the system. But we were soon out of Luton and on our way to the airport.

Relieved the boredom by singing along to my Neil Sedaka tapes, drumming on my meal tray with my plastic knife and fork and having a bit of harmless fun with the stewardesses.

India here I come!

---

*(Though not necessarily of the variety which are entered in the score-book!)

25 October
Delhi

Arrived at the hotel fairly well knackered to find a fax at Reception telling me that Nikki and the dogs had been killed in a car crash. Great laugh when I found out it was just the lads winding me up. Had a few beers with Shagger and poured a bowl of Bombay mix over Spamhead for old time's sake. Herbie's in the squad which could spell trouble; he's almost as mad about *Doctor Who* as I am about *Blake's Seven*! Later on we ran round the lobby waving our bats and going 'Errr! Cockroaches!' This has given me just the confidence I need to go out and do myself justice where it matters i.e. on the park.

26 October

On a gruelling tour like this it's essential to acclimatize as soon as possible. So, this morning it was straight down to the pool to try on our pastel-coloured Bermuda shorts and get the feel of our Wilbur Smiths. Actually, I'm going to be using a sponsored Len Deighton throughout the tour – it'll take some getting used to but that's the commercial reality of the modern game, I'm afraid.

Some of the batsmen practised leaning backwards and suddenly opening their eyes very wide.

27 October

Kept up the work rate this morning with a brainstorming session in the teamroom. Herbie, who's been here before, felt that we shouldn't be too rigid in our plans so we decided not to fix the venue for the fancy-dress party until nearer to Christmas.

Urine Man said we should have stupid forfeits for being Welsh and stuff like that. Reasonable idea.

The Manager said the Indians have got a couple of spinners but he can't remember their names or what they bowl. He reckons they're crap anyway.

29 October

East Zone Under-21s v England. England lost by an innings and 54 runs.

I struggled badly in our second innings. Just couldn't seem to get into my Len Deighton. It's about Dysart and he's going to Frankfurt, only he's got to wait and see as it all depends on Gruber. Perhaps it'll get better when I've read some more pages. Tied Shagger's bed to a sheet and hung it out the window.

30 October

Did nothing.

1 November
Relaxed.

2 November
Relaxed in the morning, did nothing in the afternoon, apologised to the couple who were standing underneath Shagger's bed when the sheet came undone.

3 November
Another bloody match tomorrow. This is becoming relentless. There was a net available but it was miles away so we did nothing and relaxed instead.

Dysart's not going to Frankfurt now as he's lost his memory.

4 November
Bangalore Over-45s 256–6, England 110 all out.
Because the game finished early, Spamhead and I went for a ride in a horse-and-cart-type effort, except with a bloke on a push-bike instead of a horse. Had a race with Benny Off Crossroads and Thirteen Amp Fuse. Roadsie and Fusey stuffed us so we poured water over our driver. Reasonable fun.

5 November
The one-dayers start soon so had a shit-or-bust spell with the Len Deighton this morning. Gruber confessed that he'd liquidated Dysart ten years ago

in Berlin, but then Dysart turns up at Frankfurt bus station with the luggage ticket in a syringe so it just makes no sense to me whatsoever. Gave up and had a net.

Discovered that if you cut a hole in the toe of your boot, your sock pokes through and flops about quite nicely.

6 November

We were looking forward to spending the day relaxing, doing nothing and getting rodent-rectummed but the Manager casually informs us that we've got to go to some torchlit ceremony with five thousand elephants which only happens once every hundred years, then on to a champagne reception in our honour at the Embassy. There's always bloody *something*. What they don't seem to understand is that we're here to play cricket.

7 November
England 86 all out. Uttar Pradesh Junior High School 90–0.

Meeting with the tour management to try and sort out the problems we're having. I admit you can't blame them for the hotel video chewing up my *Blake's Seven* tapes, but the amount of travelling and cricket is completely ridiculous. Also, we're none of us happy with the Bermuda shorts we've been given – they're just not bright enough. The

Manager says he'll send for some electric pink and green patches for us to stick on but I'll believe that when I see it. Most of us are praying for an earthquake or a plague or a presidential assassination so's we can all just go home. Why is it always the players who have to suffer?

9 November
One-Day International
India won by ten wickets.

If you put me on the spot, I'd have to hold up my hand and say that I gave it away this afternoon, or exchanged it anyway; Spamhead had finished his Leslie Thomas and he'd never read a Len Deighton so it seemed like a reasonable swap. Read the first eleven pages but then it was the same old story: I get into double figures and then lose concentration. This tour has turned into all my worst nightmares come true.

11 November
England v India One-day International.
Rain stopped play after 18 overs.
Under the new experimental regulations,
New Zealand win the match by an innings
and 73 runs.

At last, we've stopped the rot!

Roadsie got a hatful, Fusey filled his boots and I nipped in with 1 for 145. History will mark this as the game where we turned the corner. We've got some new Bermuda shorts, our stubble has got past the nasty itchy stage and we're really starting to click as a unit. I've swapped the Leslie Thomas for a Jeffrey Archer. What can you say? The guy's just a phenomenal writer. Obviously, I've had to stick the Len Deighton cover round the front, though, to keep the sponsors happy.

12 November

An unbelievable night. Everyone still bubbling from yesterday so we had a fry-up in the team-room. Benny Off Crossroads decided to make a cup of tea, which seemed like a reasonable idea – except what he didn't know was that Fusey and me had filled the kettle with sugar! So Roadsie had to solemnly empty the kettle before he could fill it up again, by which time we were in stitches. Well, after much pontification, he finally managed to successfully brew up a pot of tea. The problem came when he tried to pour it out, whereupon he discovered that the teapot had been carefully superglued to the table by none other than Messrs. Herbie, Urine Man, Spamhead, Shagger, Fusey and yours truly. We were so hilarious we couldn't even eat our biscuits. In eighteen years in the game it was the best night I've ever had. Morale is sky-bloody-high.

19 November
Eleventh One Day International.
England absent ill.

It had to happen, didn't it? Eight of us went down with the runs this morning (and I don't mean the particular variety which are entered in the score-book!!) I don't understand it. Since the tour started we've hardly eaten anything except the saveloys and fishcakes that Herbie brought from his local chippie in Chelmsford five weeks ago. I dread to think what would have happened if we'd touched any of the local grub. Most likely we'd *all* be running quick singles along the hotel corridors (though not, alas, of the particular variety which are entered in the scorebook!!!)

21 November
First Test. Bombay. England 40 for 9 at close of first day.

Someone's got to go out and do a massive job for England tomorrow (and I don't mean the parti-cular variety you flush down the toilet!!!!).

The test side ended up being: Urine Man (Capt.), Roadsie, Fusey, Ted Dexter, the physio, Dermot Reeve's mum, some lads from Stevenage and E.W. Swanton of the *Daily Telegraph*. In retrospect you'd have to say that Swanton was a bit of a risky pick. Then again, he can sometimes turn a game with that big, fuck-off pull shot.

22 November

Disaster! We're well and truly in the cart now: the trunk with all the fancy dress costumes has gone missing. This is all we need on top of everything else.

Fairly predictable media response to our losing the Test inside two days. What they don't understand is that *somebody* had to win and unfortunately it can't always be England.

29 November
Second Test. First Day.

To be fair, Reevesie's mum is the only one of us in any serious nick at the moment. Nevertheless I was very disappointed to be told at breakfast that she'd got The Nod ahead of me for the bits-and-pieces slot. Busied myself with the usual Twelfth Man duties: driving the drinks wagon in a zig-zag, carrying funny hats on to the field, pretending to be blind etc. Also had a reasonable spell standing on the balcony with a towel round my waist.

3 December

Lost the Second Test. Had a burger. Drew a beggar.

9 December
Third Test. Jaipur.
India 765–2. Match abandoned due to rioting.
We've apologised to the Indian Cricket Board and
promised that the lads won't get out of order
again.

18 December
Fourth Test. Fifth Day.
England (first innings) 342 for 4. Match drawn.
I don't understand the media. We've just had five
days of the most pulsating test cricket you could
hope for – 70-odd runs a day, a wicket every 36
hours and a very close leg-before shout on the

Friday. What more do they want? They watch too much one-day cricket, that's their problem.

22 December
Fifth Test. Calcutta. First day.
Unbelievable! The fancy dress costumes have been impounded in Amsterdam and they won't be here in time for Christmas. Just my luck it should happen on the day I get The Nod ahead of Mrs Reeve (who was beginning to find the pressures of Test cricket a bit too much). We decided not to take the field until we had a full apology from the Indian Government plus some false beards and togas and a Shirley Bassey outfit. I was desperately disappointed not to be savouring the atmosphere of the larger arena but a principle is a principle and I think we're right to make a stand.

23 December
Fifth Test. Second Day.
Spend a ridiculous morning hanging round the pavilion not knowing if the game was on or off and without the remotest clue as to what we'd be wearing at the Christmas party. It was total Fred Karno's. We finally received a fax at noon: a typical Lord's climbdown. They told us we had to play, fancy dress or no fancy dress. Whose side are they on? Once again proof that this is a game for professionals run by amateurs.

25 December
Fifth Test. Rest Day.

If you put what happened today in a Boy's Own fairytale storybook written by Jeffrey Archer you'd still say it was unbelievable! But there it is in the record books for all time: 5th Test, Calcutta. Winner of fancy dress contest: D. V. Podmore (Lawrence of Arabia).

Don't know what it was that gave me the idea of going into town to find a tailor. Just one of those reflex things that either come off or they don't.

The egg-heads in the press box tell me it was only the ninth Lawrence of Arabia outfit in Anglo-Indian tests and, apparently, I'm the first Nottinghamshire-born player to wear a winning costume on debut etc. etc. Boys' Own stuff as I say.

Look out Sri Lanka! Pod's on a roll (and I don't mean the particularly variety that's manufactured by Messrs. Andrex!!!!!).

DAVE PODMORE IN TEST CRICKET

England v Sri Lanka. Colombo. 1992.

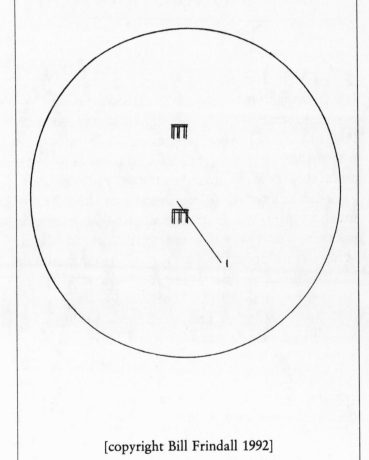

[copyright Bill Frindall 1992]

10

POD IN PERFORMANCE

I often think that being a county cricketer is very like being a great actor or an opera singer such as Pavarotti. You have an audience, you have a stage (the park), you get slagged off by the media and you go for a curry afterwards. It's virtually the same job.

I have always regarded myself as a showman as much as a bits-and-pieces specialist who can bung up an end and give it some tap in a run drought. What the public want, be they at The Coliseum or be they at Colwyn Bay is not just a smartly turned-out professional (although neatness is important), they are looking to be entertained. Some of my tricks like pretending to be blind, walking on to the pitch with an umbrella, taking off a coloured chap, and running in to bowl without the ball in my hand are among the best-loved features of an English summer. Obviously, it is nice to be known as the Clown Prince of Cricket but, the way I see it, I am really only doing my job.

With my extensive collection of co-ordinated fashion knitwear, I have a reputation for handling media appearances fairly easily. But believe me, it hasn't all been plaudits and bouquets for Dave Podmore. Whenever I fill in a media questionnaire, there is never any problem answering the 'Most Embarrassing Moment' section. Opening the batting in that department is my first appearance on *A Question of Sport*. You may remember it. Oh dear!

To say I lost the plot would be an understatement. I was fine until they played the opening music then I suddenly went into a cold sweat. By the time Coleman introduced me my mouth was as dry as a Somerset towel. When he asked me how the season was going I just froze. Could I remember what county I played for? I couldn't even remember my name. If Diane Modahl hadn't come to my rescue I think they would have had to start the show all over again.

If I could only have got off the mark I think I would have been all right and I got very close a couple of times with the darts questions. The most frustrating part of the evening was the mystery sportsperson section. I knew straightaway it was Spamhead from the specks of dandruff on the snooker table but Beaumont reckoned it was Flo-Jo and there was no point trolleying with him because he's the skipper and he can give you a bad report. So that was it – I drove all that way to Manchester and I didn't even get a single point.

Afterwards I was so gutted I felt like bursting out crying. It wasn't the losing that hurt, it was knowing I hadn't done myself justice. I was far too depressed to go to the hospitality room. But then Merlene Ottey sat me down and said I'd done all right and some of the audience had laughed at my crack about Waqar Younis being an anagram of 'You is wanqar', and anyway, she said, she'd made a **** of herself on her first programme. So she took me to the bar and got a few beers down me and Both tipped a bowl of crisps over me and after a bit I didn't feel too bad.

It actually turned into one of the great nights – at least I think it did! I can just about remember bogging off to Rusholme for the mother of all ring-burners with Jackie Ageypong and Alvin Schoko-moeller, but I'm afraid it's all a bit of a blur after that.

Whenever I've been in the frame for higher media honours, I've found that, time and time again *A Question of Sport* has been held against me. Anyone can have an off day, it seems, as long as his name doesn't happen to be Dave Podmore Esquire. Once again it's a case of D.V.P. being behind the eight ball as far as getting a fair deal is concerned.

I shall never forget Jacqui's tear-stained face when I came home from modelling some abdominal protectors at Gunn & Moore's. She had been watching TV and it had just come up on Ceefax that Gareth Chilcott had got The Nod for *Aladdin* at the Theatre Royal, Bath. 'It just isn't fair, Pod,' she wailed, 'What more d'you have to do?' I don't think theatre managers realize the effect their decisions have on people sometimes. There's only one word for that kind of behaviour; it starts with an 's', it ends with a 'd' and it's got an 'a' in between (sad).

When the panto call eventually came in 1992 it all happened in such a rush there was no time to celebrate. One of the lads from The Fenn Street Gang had to pull out of *Mother Goose* at the last minute and I was invited to step into the breach. I would have preferred to go in as first choice but it still gave me a tremendous high to know that, at long last, I was on my way – to the Conquest Theatre, Bromyard.

Pantomime has been a central part of my winter activities ever since. It's a fantastic challenge to your stamina and your commitment has to be 350% minimum. It's one thing playing Shane Warne on a bunsen at Brisbane, but you want to try picking June Whitfield on a Wednesday matinée when she's on song. It is a different ball game. Although they both wear a lot of make up, obviously.

Panto is all about fitness, really. You're doing two shows a day and in some of those big theatres you could be throwing bags of sweets to kiddies maybe thirty or forty yards away. With a work rate like that it's all too easy to pick up a niggle. As a matter of fact, I believe that was how David Gower lost his throwing arm. It's tragic when a great performer ends up lobbing everything under-arm into the stalls. That was more or less what happened to me when I was doing a matinée of *Pod In Boots* at the Hexagon Theatre, Slough, a couple of Christmases back. The same kiddie in the front row ended up with twenty-five packets of Monster Munch and nobody else got a look in. I had to be stretchered off before the finale. Fortunately, Mark Ramprakash was rehearsing *Lady Windermere's Fan* at Windsor at the time (he's a class act, is Ramps), so luckily he was was able to take over for the second house.

I was very satisfied with my performance in *Pod In Boots*, and after the success of the show I thought I'd done enough to take the step up into the larger arena. Unfortunately, the manager of the Arena would only offer me the same money as I got at the Hexagon – which has 227 fewer seats (explain the logic of that if you can!). Yet again it was a case of me being led up a blind Panto alley.

Ray Poole sized up the situation immediately. He sat me down in the Sportsman's Bar at the Moat House, looked me straight in the eye and said, 'Listen Pod, if we don't have a crack at

Hollywood now we may miss the boat.' I thought he was being ridiculous but he has a very persuasive manner sometimes has R. Poole Esquire. So earlier this year we embarked on what could be the most exciting development in my career to date.

Universal Studios is an amazing place and they certainly pulled out all the stops for Ray and myself. I felt like I was a film star as soon as I arrived. We were met at the gates by a guy dressed as Dracula (probably one of the top executives) who showed us round with some other people. Then I had to do my screen test which was incredibly interesting. They sat me on ET's bike and I read some lines with a moon behind me. They didn't give me a contract as such but I got a certificate which Ray says amounts to the same thing. It was quite an expensive trip but Ray says I will get it all back once he starts talking turkey to Universal's Mr Big.

There's nothing concrete yet but Ray says we should be hearing something very soon, so *Pod of Arabia*? *Thelma and Louise and Pod*? Who knows? Sean Connery, watch out!

HIGHLIGHTS OF MY LIFE

Steaming in to Dad!
Glapwell Recreation
Ground, 1956

Full of East Midlands promise . . .
one of Wisden's Five Young
Cricketers of the Year, 1972

Dad's Final Delivery -
Dust to dust, ashes to ball!

To Pod
From Potters

Pol Pot -
someone I'm proud to call a friend

GOING INTO BATTLE

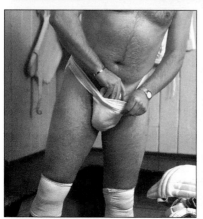

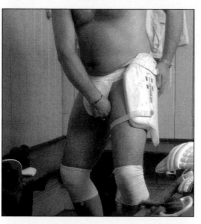
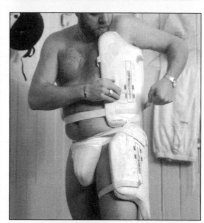
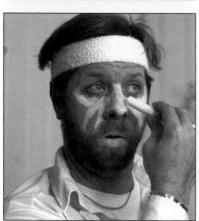

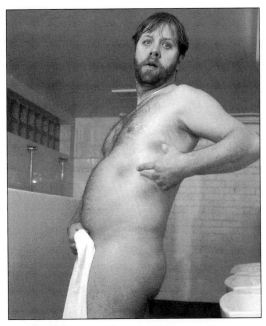

Bruised but Unbowed after a sustained
onslaught from Daffy (DeFreitas) in the
showers - a demon with a new towel in his
hand.

Caught in Two Man's Land! It
can happen to anyone, even the
best.

D. V. P. forges another
successful partnership with
1987 sponsor Gorden Treen,
head honcho of Duraflex
Ladders (East Midlands Div.)

IN THE NETS AT THE PODMORE ACADEMY OF EXCELLENCE

PUTTING THE YOUNGSTERS THROUGH THEIR PACES

Timing is all about balance. Wrong . . .

. . . Right. Always keep your eye on the target.

It's all in the wrists . . . whichever side you're on in the Jug vs Straight Glass debate. Nice Panatella skills from Warren (left).

Bombay Mix in the batting glove - a classical stroke to pull!

Tim (left) puts it in the slot - itching powder in the jock will get even the greatest batsmen hopping around!

Gutted! The fancy dress costumes have gone missing.
The lads take the news badly.

Crack open the bubbly!
Stewie's found a novelty shop in Bangalore.

My finest hour. Can you spot Podmore of Arabia?

FLASHPOINT!

WORKSOP, 1994

There or Thereabouts

How . . .

. . . Was . . .

. . . That??

I don't ****ing
Believe It!

Pod demonstrating why having
a Third Umpire is essential in
the modern game.

DEAR UMPIRE,
I'M SORRY ~~₦~~ FOR
THE KICKING I GIVE
YOU.
SIGNED
Pod

THE LADIES IN MY LIFE

Nikki with the Laughing Eyes (in the days when she had a sense of humour)

Toni - A Great Way To Fly . . . till the wheels came off.

Dave and Jacqui Podmore - what a great pair (and I'm not referring to the feathered variety!)

PERKS OF THE JOB!

Going for a Drive (not the batting variety)

Mr Mobile, 21st century style, calling Ray Poole on the Internet.

My Other Car's a Nissan Bluebird 1.6GS (without hatchback)

The name's POD . . . JAMES POD.

Licensed to Murder a Curry! Another great Ray Poole brainwave.

POD IN BOOTS

① ☺

SCENE ONE: OUTSIDE THE BLUE BOAR INN.
CHORUS IN GINGHAM DRESSES, DUNGAREES, PICNIC BASKETS ETC.

OPENING NUMBER 'It's a Lovely Day Today'.

Sweeting @ ten grand ₤ ✗
10,000 ₤
50000 ₤

CHORUS BOY: You know, I've been thinking, everyone. I'm
not sure it <u>is</u> such a lovely day after all.
The wicked Baron Jessie 'Eldorado' Birdsall is
going to throw us all out of our homes.

₤128000
50,000
₤178,000

Halifax
3·log

CHORUS: Oh no. (GIRLS LEAN FORWARD, BOYS TUCK THEIR THUMBS
IN THEIR BRACES) We wish there was someone who could
save us and hit that pesky Baron for six.

Nationwide
3-688

BAND PLAYS THE TEST MATCH SPECIAL THEME.

**ENTER POD WEARING MEDIEVAL CLOTHES BUT WITH PADS AND GLOVES
ETC.** *walk to the middle. Stop at the mark*

CHORUS: Hooray, it's Pod. Owzat!

POD: Owzat! Hello boys and girls! ✗ ✗ It's great to be back in *some HELMET OFF HERE*
Slough although I've never scored much here - not on the
pitch anyway! ✗✗ I hope my balls are all right. *Cont.*

CHORUS BOY: Please, Pod, you've just got to help us.

Droitwich
Magistrate's Court
17th Jan. 9.1

POD: ✓ Oh very well. But you know, you don't have to have *put hand on Winston's shoulder*
money to be rich. *Turn radio mike off*

**BAND PLAYS 'I'VE GOT THE SUN IN THE MORNING AND THE MOON AT
NIGHT'. GARY SINGS OFFSTAGE, POD MIMES.** *Dance: 00 0₀ 0 P   00 repeat*
Radio mike back on now

POD: Now to bowl the Baron middle stump. Oh, but I was
forgetting. I haven't got anything to hit him for six
with. And anyway, it's just too far away. I wish I
could help you boys and girls but...

Wed Matinee
2 tickets for
Graham Roope

CHORUS: What about this wishing well? *✓ reach into it.*

POD: All right, I'll give it a try. FLASH ✓ Fantastic! A *g..... 3y*
brand new Gunn and Moore Turbo-fibre Magnum Ultraflex
bat! FLASH I can't believe it - I'll get to the
Baron's castle in no time in this superb Nissan Bluebird
Premium from Ray Poole (Nissan) of Hinckley. Off we go.

CHORUS GIRL: (WITH ONE HAND ON HER HIP) Oh Pod. You've
still got one wish left.

POD: In that case I'd like to hear Ronnie Hylton singing his
1963 hit single 'A Mouse in Old Amsterdam' *Drive off hooting horn.*

BAND PLAYS RONNIE'S INTRO

11

PODDERS STARKERS!

'So there I was in the hotel corridor, the lift doors opened and a party of eight nuns were confronted by the awesome spectacle of D. V. Podmore – and you won't believe this – FULLY CLOTHED!!'

Okay, I'll come clean – I made that one up! Because, to be perfectly honest, I'm the first to admit that not many anecdotes about my antics on and off the park have ended like this. What? Rooming on tour with Foxy Fowler and with Beef and Embers a couple of doors away? Come off it! Adding it up, I suppose that I've spent over thirty hours of my professional career (or a full test match's playing time) inappropriately and more often than not embarrassingly naked.

Like a lot of things in my life, it was a skill learnt early on, to be precise at Number 46 Gibraltar Road, Mablethorpe. This was where I spent some of the most halcyon days of my childhood, courtesy of Halcyon Days Minibreaks, Sutton-In-Ashfield. One morning on the sands, Dad (Dave Senior), found a shilling in a bather's discarded plimsoll and treated us all, buying me a '99' ice-cream cornet. I decided that the best way to show my gratitude was to go one better in that day's play and notch up my first beach century!

Sadly, when it was time to go back to the digs, Dad was out of pocket. I'd been trying to emulate Sir Garry Sobers, who that summer had humiliated Glamorgan's Malcolm Nash, taking six sixes off him in one over and forcing him to give up cricket altogether and join the pop group The Hollies. Two tennis balls had to be bought after I'd started hitting them out of the ground (into the sea), and, though the third new ball was a solid rubber one attached to elastic – giving me a better-than-even chance of recording a Fastest Ton Ever – Mum by this time had had enough and lifted her finger.

My punishment was not, as you might expect, going without supper (that was considered Getting a Result back at 15, Foundry Lane!), but standing stock-still outside the front door of the digs until dawn without the benefit of protective jim-jams. There was a cold wind blowing off the North Sea that night, but luckily I was protected from the worst of it by the fact that Gibraltar Road is sheltered underneath the sand-dunes. I also recognized that it was good for my character, so I didn't blub or take legal action, I just got on with it and the next day made sure that all my strokes went along the ground down the leg-side!

There's probably enough of that little boy left in the deep recesses of my mind to make me realise subconsciously that wrong-doing should automatically be followed by me getting my kit off. This is venturing into pretty deep water, of course, and, as you must know by now, Dave Podmore prefers life at the Shallow End, where you can reach out and pull Tim Robinson in off his sun lounger, with no harm done except a waterlogged Walkman! Professor Mike Brearley would no doubt have enough material for one of his treatises, and Judgey's hypnotist could fill up a half-hour programme before the Lottery with what makes me expose myself at every opportunity. But, there you are. I do it and I have to live with it.

I suppose the most famous occasion was in the mid-Seventies when half-way through the Trent Bridge Test it suddenly became clear that England had a shout of regaining the Ashes. I was lucky enough to be playing for Notts that year and even luckier to find myself promoted to Twelfth Man duties! This came about through a real ill-wind situation (and I don't mean of the variety produced after a good night in Derek Randall's 'Ayup Me Crispy Duck' Chinese restaurant!) The Notts first team had all gone off to a studio in town to record their singalong version of *Robin Hood*, and, somehow, had neglected to tell me which one. Suddenly I found a drinks tray being thrust into my hands and I was told to get out there and do a job for my country.

Swimming before my eyes were all the soft drink colours of the rainbow (there was a special low-calorie Irn Bru for Mike Denness, I seem to remember). Hands shaking, knees knocking, I ventured gingerly down the steps . . . then up again as I'd gone down a flight too far, into the Gents by mistake! My only regret was that my dad wasn't there in the stands to see me, but he swore to me afterwards that he felt a tingle down his spine as he sat fishing that afternoon on the banks of the River Erewash.

What happened next is best summed up by the doyen of commentators, Jim Laker, on a tape that I run over and over again in my head (and which some of my crueller colleagues run over and over again on the dressing-room video).

'Oh and he's dropped it! I just do not believe it – he's put it down! There's barley water all over the pitch, the tray's flattened the wicket, broken glass everywhere . . . Arthur Fagg's picking a frozen jubbly out of his pocket . . . just as England were about to regain the ascendancy! They're going to have to call it off, this is an absolute disaster! It's "George Davis is Innocent" all over again!'

Sure, I panicked. But you have to look at what happened next from my point of view. It seemed to me in that split-second that the only thing to do was to give the crowd some distraction and defuse a possibly ugly situation by showing my bum. Which I duly did, not to mention the rest of my anatomy. As it happens, the heavens opened after what would have been the scheduled tea interval, and the next two days would have been completely washed out anyway, so there was no real damage done.

And one interesting knock-on effect came after England *didn't* regain the Ashes. Several disgruntled players broke away from the official team as Mr Kerry Packer entered the fray, bestowing his largesse on almost everyone in the game except the bits-and-pieces county cricketer. I rejoice that in my own small way I have helped to make many of my colleagues richer.

But what you want to hear is more tales of Pod flashing his goolies. The next memorable occasion was after a Saturday's play at Headquarters, when I came in late on as Night Watchman for Glamorgan, or it may have been Northants. This is a much underrated role, the batsman who can stick around for an hour and a half or so until stumps, frustrating opposition and crowd alike as he nurdles the very occasional single and holds up play by refastening the straps on his pads. It's often rewarded by a Not Out score followed by an overnight declaration. These invaluable runs can accumulate over the season into ninety-odd for maybe twice out, a healthy position there or thereabouts at the top of the averages and a renewal of a contract for next year. Not surprisingly, the job of Night Watchman is one Dave Podmore covets.

Anyway, as I say, we were playing on the Hallowed Turf up there in St. Johns Wood, NW8 8QN, and the lads were all eager to get off the field, shower, and head out West to the New London Theatre where *Cats* was (and at the time of writing still is) packing them in. Just how eager, I became aware out there in the middle, when there was the unmistakable sound of slow-handclapping coming from the Players' Balcony! In my defence I would have to say that I was building up a painstaking twelve not out, which would push my average into double figures for the first time that season. This I achieved as the famous hands of Old Father Time passed seven o'clock, and as I left the field clutching my celebratory stump I realised that I was completely alone at Lord's.

A moment for deep contemplation, I think you'll agree. In fact I must have slipped into something not unakin to a reverie, because when I happened to glance at my watch in the otherwise deserted showers (something I often do, as it works under water) I realized to my horror that *Cats* would be kicking off in less than twenty minutes.

Stopping only to cover my modesty with a towel, I ran out of the Grace Gates and jumped into a passing taxi. It was already taken and I found myself in the company of an amply-proportioned blonde lady. Pod is nothing if not red-blooded, and I had to quickly concentrate not on my beauteous companion but other more mundane matters in order to avoid seepage under the covers, so to speak! Watching Chris Old even up his sideboards . . . listening to Gatt pontificate on who was the best Doctor Who . . . a day out at Wellingborough – these seemed to do the trick and I arrived in Drury Lane with honour intact.

Unfortunately, as the cab door slammed behind me my towel got caught in it, so there I was, in the foyer, once again exposed to the elements, not to mention a bevy of fur-coated theatre-goers! Fortunately, a young usher (and trainee dancer as I later found out over a drink with him) came to my rescue, hiding my blushes and other things besides with a tray of programmes and Maltesers. And the lads filled me in afterwards on what I'd missed Old Possum-wise, so no harm done.

Then there was the time (and you may have read something about this in the papers!) I was challenged by 'Deadly' Derek Underwood to join the 'Five Mile High Club' on a Jumbo Jet during a

John Snow Tour to the Far East. The catch was that there wasn't one, but *two* amply-proportioned stewardesses waiting in toilets at opposite ends of the plane! I'm afraid to say the full story of this will have to wait for the paperback edition of the book – it's what they call *sub-judice* in legal circles, as my fight against extradition to Libya (in whose air-space we were flying at the time) is still going on. But it seemed funny then.

THE DAVE PODMORE MASTERCLASS

12

CONTROVERSY!

A question that came up not so long ago in an interview with my good friend Andy Hamer (of BBC Radio Leicester's 'Andy Hamer in the Afternoon') was 'What would Dave Podmore say had been the most controversial moment in his career?' And when I'd worked out that Andy was asking *me*, I was, for once, stuck for an answer. Because, quite frankly, such moments are almost too numerous to mention. But I'll do my best.

I suppose one of the first occasions that my name came to the attention of the media-buying public was in the late '70s, over the vexed question of what headgear to wear to best combat the danger posed by the West Indian quicks. England skipper Mike Brearley came in for much (to my mind unfair) flak over his bold decision to wear a pink rubber contraption that fitted under his cap and came down over his ears. Unfair because it wasn't generally realised that Mike was sponsored by Durex at the time.

But I decided to cut through the cr*p and recognize that, yes, those guys *were* faster than anything seen before on English soil, and therefore some retaliatory action had to be taken. I duly took the field for Leicestershire vs West Indies in 1976 wearing a pair of what came to be called 'beeny-boppers', bouncing balls on stalks that sent a 'You don't frighten me, man' message up to Michael Holding or whoever was steaming in at the other end of the track. The authorities took a dim view, not for the first time, and from then on it was helmets or nothing.

Once again I was ahead of my time. Just look at the recent rise of groups of supporters taking their seats dressed up as nuns, or Vikings, or all wearing pink wigs. This I feel has done nothing but add much-needed colour and attractiveness to the game, as well as giving the cameras something to cut away to while Martin McCague is bowling.

But, when I try to take the field wearing the letters 'O.V.' sun-blocked on to my face – as I am contractually obliged so to do by my sponsors, Oadby Vintners – then, once again, it's a case of, 'Oh dearie me no, Mr Podmore – you're bringing the game into disrepute. So no supper and early bed for you, my fine friend.' Proof again, if proof were needed, that this is a game of professionals run by amateurs.

Here's another case in point. Headingley 1981. To cricket-lovers everywhere that England/Australia Test is burned indelibly into the record books. In the dark winter months those lucky enough to have been there still warm their hands against the memory, and talk in awed tones of one lone Englishman and the single act of daring that sums up all that's best in our national character: the guy who put the bets on an England win at 500-1 for Dennis Lillee and Rodney Marsh!

It should have been me. I'd been doing some promotional work for the Bowater-Atwater Group in Leeds that Monday morning, and I popped into the ground after lunch to witness what I confidently expected to be another England débâcle, bringing about some head-scratching on the Selectors' Balcony and the long-overdue decision to opt for new blood.

'C'm here, you pommie bastard,' came the unmistakeable tones of Lillee behind me as I headed round the back of the pavilion in search of a sausage roll.

'Po*dd*ie bastard, if you don't mind,' I came back, faster than even the tall West Australian could bowl in his prime. I'm fairly sure that endeared me to him straight away, as the ensuing conversation proved.

'Get your fat arse round the Ladbrokes tent and stick this pony on England at a monkey, you galah.'

He handed me five fivers. I ventured to suppose that part of it was my commission.

'Is it b*ll*cks. But I'll give you an autographed copy of my new tin bat.'

This seemed like a bargain to me – I'd heard of the 'Com-Bat' and thought it was just the sort of forward marketing thinking we could have done with in the English game. Not to mention doing away with many boring hours spent treating the traditional Gunn & Moore job with linseed oil in the winter, when now just a quick wipe with a J-cloth would do the trick. I held my hand out, Dennis spat on it and the deal was done.

Sadly, the bet was not to be: on my way past the Rugby League ground I noticed that a hoarding advertising Bowater-Atwater, my sponsors, had fallen flat on its back, out of sight of the TV cameras. Duty called, and by the time I'd put it back up again and got to the betting tent, the odds on an England win had shrunk to 125–1 – obviously there were lots of like-minded sports-men around. I assessed the situation and kept the money, surmising that there was no way England could salvage the situation. Not for the first time, I had reckoned without a certain superhuman being going under the name of I.T. Botham!

I subsequently discovered that Lillee had had an 'each-way' bet, deciding not to trust me and getting someone else to put some more money on. Fair enough if that's the way he wanted to play it. Typical Aussie mentality, and it did at least get me off the hook. I thought it prudent however to grow my moustache and beard just to be on the safe side, and spent the rest of the '80s thus attired face-wise.

Echoes of Headingley came back to me some

years later — not only did I enjoy the spectacle of D. K. Lillee Esq. puffing round the outfield during his brief spell with Northants. ('Who's the fat-arse now?' I thought), I also pulled off a bit of a betting coup of my own, backing England to lose the 1985/6 series against the Windies 5-0, for which I obtained the not ungenerous odds of 3-to-1. Once again a certain I. T. Botham didn't let me down!

True, I got a fair amount of stick for this from so-called England loyalists, but, as far as I was concerned, the benefit cheque was mine to do what I liked with. With the proceeds I was in fact able to buy the patch of land at the back of the 'Poderosa' and build the kennels on it, so I think it's fair to say that, on this occasion, cricket was the winner.

This section would of course be incomplete without my side of what I said to Her Majesty that day at Arundel when we were all lined up with the 1977 Australian tourists. In my own defence I have to make clear that I only said it to win a bet with Ashley Mallett. And, in any case, I'm fairly confident that she can't pretend she hasn't heard as bad or worse from Prince Philip over the years.

Having said that, your Majesty, I'm sorry if it spoiled your Jubilee Year. I'd like to apologise in person and am willing to meet you any place, any time . . . with a slight preference for Sandringham now that the new A14 is open and it's a clear run through from Oadby.

* * *

POETRY CORNER

'Poetry' and 'Podmore' aren't often mentioned in the same breath. I have to agree, but I do have my romantic side. I remember once giving Expert Summaries on a Sunday League match for Sky TV. Of course I assumed nobody was watching and was duly caught out by Charles Colvile drawing little birds and flowers on the screen, instead of arrows telling the viewers where backward short-leg was! As Brian Bolus used to say to me at Derby: 'Don't assume anything, Pod – it makes an ass of you and me.' Brylcreemed old bastard, bless him.

But here's my personal tribute to one of the greatest writers the game's ever known – Sir Henry Newbolt. A few hundred years ago he wrote about a certain funny old game (or a funny new game as it was then). I've taken a bit of poetic licence with the words of course, but I like to think that if he read them, Newbolty wouldn't be totally gutted.

There's a Diarrhoea Finish on the park tonight,
Daffy's bowling, and he's cat's arse tight!
The last man gobs, and he goes like that*
The short leg's in and he calls him a twat,

The batsman plays – the air is rent
There's Baywatch on in the Ladbrokes' tent
There's a glint on the windscreen of the sponsored car,
The Tandoori's open in half an hour.

And it's not for the sake of a third-round tie,
Or a place in the rankings from Whyte and Mackay.
An over to go, we still need eight . . .
We're off – it's raining. F*cking great!

[Copyright Ray Poole (Verse) Hinckley, 1995]

* A readjustment of the box, signifying 'I mean business'

* * *

JUST CALL ME POD-ASSO!

"A country cottage"

Like a lot of cricketers, I find painting watercolours very relaxing. My style's changed over the seasons – I began in the traditional Victorian style ...

"Achtung! Death at Tobruk"

... until the anniversary of World War II came along, when I realized what those guys had gone through to get a result for their country ...

... now my work combines these 'genres' in a style I feel
is all my own

"Bombed Country Cottage"

*   *   *

13

POD'S PARTNERSHIPS

MARITAL STATUS: Divorced from Toni, Nikki; currently happily engaged to Jacqui, despite what you might read in the media.

They say every statistic tells a story worth a thousand words, but as far as yours truly is concerned that bald entry in the *Cricketers' Who's Who* is only the tip of the iceberg. Sure, I have the reputation of not being exactly a saint (and I'm not talking of the Roger Moore variety!), but when it comes to the Ladies in Lake Podmore, the truth is a double-edged Excalibur indeed.

Spending twenty-three consecutive years on the county circuit (not to mention regularly driving from Chester-le-Street to Abergavenny for the Zonal rounds of the Tilcon Trophy) means a heckuva lot of wear and tear on more than just your tyres. Luckily, as far as the car is concerned, my long-standing arrangement with Ray Poole

(Nissan) of Hinckley means I'm never short of a new set of radials.

Unfortunately, the same can't be said of my personal life, and I sometimes think it would save an awful lot of trouble if there were such a thing as a 'Marriage Garage', where I could drop mine off for servicing, borrow a courtesy replacement and collect the original, recharged and with a new coat of paint, four days later! Anyway, here's *my* side of the stories that have been floating round the dressing-rooms for a few years now, polluting the atmosphere worse than one of Lamby's post-ruby murray ripsnorters!

TONI

Everyone's allowed to make one mistake (unless your name happens to be A. Test Selector, Esquire, which means you're allowed an infinite number) and getting married to Toni too young was Dave Podmore's. I mentioned in 'Early Doors' that we first met on the plane transporting me to the Under-14s Tour of the West Indies, and Toni saved me a lot of potential embarrassment, quickly wiping the milk off my tie after one of those plastic pots had spurted out the way they do whichever way you try to open them (future visitors to my Benefit Tent may rest assured that my marketing team and I are working against the clock to obliterate this nuisance, along with packets of digestive biscuits that involve the use of teeth).

But, deep down, I think we knew it was always going to be a bit of a limited-overs marriage, and the wheels really fell off with the discovery (when he turned up on the doorstep) that I'd accidentally fathered a 17-year-old coloured son called Eustace on that same tour, after a less than ruly night of roistering in Barbados led by a certain Master I. T. Botham! To be fair to me though, it really should have been Goodnight Vienna Toni-wise long before that.

As far as I'm concerned, the rot set in when she started getting big ideas and applied to Hinckley Hairdressing College, now of course the East Midlands Hair University. This often kept her out late at night, learning how to deal with tricky partings apparently, and I soon noticed the absence of a cooked meal waiting for me when I came back after a hard day in the field, as did the dogs. Of course, when the boot was on the other foot it was a different matter, and I well remember the Mount Rushmore face I'd get from Toni if I so much as walked in half an hour after Closing Time!

It so happened that on that particular occasion I'd decided to have a 'net' for my forthcoming appearance on *A Question of Sport* and dropped in on a local pub quiz, where I picked up some useful titbits I would otherwise have forgotten, such as the names of the firemen in Trumpton. But not even this genuine excuse cut any ice with the first Mrs P.

'Why don't you apply to go on *Mastermind* instead?' opined Her Royal Highbrowness.

'Any suggestions for my Special Subject?' I replied.

She was ready for that.

'How about the motorway system of England, starting from Oadby?'

You see what I was up against. And when Toni even started hinting that my participation in big-hearted Beefy Botham's Leukaemia Walk was nothing more than a Leukaemia Pub Crawl, I realized it was Sayonara time.

NIKKI

I can't pretend making the transition from my first to my second wife was easy: for starters, there being one more letter in 'Nikki' than 'Toni' meant less peripheral driving vision due to the longer name on the windscreen. But that was a mere fly in the ointment compared to the breath of fresh air Nikki brought into my life, from that first meeting at Trent Bridge when she was a Rothmans Personality

Girl and I was opening the Dave Podmore Temporary Stand (no prizes for guessing who it was named after!).

Nikki even put up with my little quirks in the kitchen, when I taped over such brand-names as 'Surf' and 'Weetabix' after my sponsorship deal with Messrs Lever Brothers fell through. She was a great girl in those days, and would get along like a house on fire with all the other players' wives like Helen Dilley, Helen Allott and Helen Ormrod, despite the obvious cultural differences.

But then along came the night of the Selina Scott Incident, which I have dealt with fully and I hope frankly in Chapter 5. One knock-on effect of which I was blissfully unaware was the keen interest which the media took in my errand of mercy to the Royal Free Hospital, to visit the bedside of that extremely attractive bachelor girl. The Press had obviously been giving Nikki a less than easy time, because when I walked into the front door of 'Thirty-Seven' she made me feel as welcome as a turd in a fruit salad (note for you cricket trivia buffs: technically my house is Number Twenty-Four, but I got special dispensation from Oadby District Council to change it from 'The Poderosa' to my highest first-class score, in return for holding one of my famous 'Pod Man Out' cricketing surgeries in the village hall. Two 'Thirty-Sevens' in the same avenue of course leads to some not unamusing situations with the post-man!).

As I say, Nikki made me feel as welcome as a hole in a lifeboat. It would be less than totally honest of me not to admit that our marriage had been going through a bad trot of late, and now it was showdown time at the O.K. Corral.

'Cool it, Nikk,' I began.

'Don't "Cool it, Nikk" me, Pod,' she snapped back. 'This isn't the first time is it, not by a long chalk. What about the recent stories involving you and a certain AXA Equity & Law Assurance hostess?'

I had to laugh. 'Hand on heart,' I said, 'I can hold the other one up and swear to you that I'd need to be Spiderman, the Incredible Hulk, Don Juan, Romeo, a JCB and Gatt rolled into one to have done the thing I was alleged to have done to her that night!'

But now the gloves were off . . . and they weren't made by Messrs Gunn & Moore. Suddenly, Nikki was raking up all kinds of ancient history. Now, I'd be the first to admit that I haven't always been a perfect father. Being away from home so much hasn't made it exactly easy, and of course I've had to go off and play cricket as well. Having said that, family life comes pretty high on my list of priorities, and you couldn't have a much better example than when our son Dave Junior was born.

Unfortunately, I couldn't be present at the birth itself as I had to attend an important boxing dinner at the Nottingham Ice Rink. But I put myself out a bit, having a phone brought to my table and ringing Nikki in hospital to tell her about the huge round of applause there'd been when they announced Dave Junior's arrival over the tannoy. Obviously it was still a bit of a sore point though – as was my flying off the handle on the 91/92 Sri Lanka Tour, when Nikki committed the (to my mind) unpardonable sin of arriving without essential dietary items.

'You mean she didn't Bring Out The Branston?' quipped Lubo, sharp as you like when he heard this disastrous news, but just then I was in no mood for his quicksilver wit. In actual fact I was in a deeply embarrassing position, having recently made the acquaintance of Roger Whitaker of whistling fame. Roj was performing at Colombo's Mrs Bandaranaike Stadium and had sent two free tickets for the gig, of which 'Picca' Dilley and I were the lucky recipients following a keenly-fought raffle. Beefy was so keen to go that he even ate my ticket and tried to have the contest declared void! Luckily Mick Jagger and Eric Idle arrived just then and hauled him off to visit a magnificent Buddhist temple they'd recently discovered.

After enjoying an evening of superb profession-alism intermingled with hilarity – Roj's impression of the Dawn Chorus being interrupted by a vinegar shaker gave me some of my best moments ever – the least I could do was try and repay his generosity. Over a backstage drink Roj had confided in me that one of the major drawbacks of appearing on the sub-continent (apart from the shambolic plumbing, needless to say!) was the difficulty of getting hold of a mild pickle, the local spicy varieties being too hard on the lips that are a whistler's stock-in-trade.

You can guess the rest: I specifically asked Nikki to include a few jars of Branston for Roj among the Marmite and Fruit Loops that I was craving . . . and she goes and forgets! Looking back, I can see that this was something of a catalyst in what was always going to be an uneasy relationship.

Fast-forward to the night of Le Big Bust-Up. Even though the house was in my name, I walked, in the 'Without-Waiting-To-Be-Given-Out' meaning of the word, and spent the night at Spamhead's, kipping down on his floor. Just to digress for a few seconds on the good ship HMS Spamhead: if you put a gun to my head and asked me to pick a team to save my life, this guy would be opening both the batting and bowling. His St. John's Ambulance First Aid Certificate would be invaluable in the case of that unfortunate eventuality, not to mention his pot-holing diploma!

I won't pretend it was easy though, those first weeks. Once, after lying awake for hours looking at a chair-leg, I even plucked up courage and gave Roger Whitaker a ring. 'Honorary Bearders' as we called him (the original nickname of course being the jealously-guarded province of scorer extraordinaire Bill Frindall) was absolutely magnificent, taking time out to listen to my troubles when he should have been embarking on a lucrative cruise. I can honestly say that Roger's soothing whistling did on that occasion help me make it through the night.

That was Arrivederci Roma for me and Nikki as you might expect, apart from the inevitably painful division of the possessions. Basically, I let her have everything except the house, its contents, the car, the dogs and my beloved set of autographed Leslie Thomases. 'Pod collecting novels?!' I can hear Frances Edmonds and her smart Women's Libber friends laugh as they knock back a bottle of Chateau Posho — but yes, that's right girls, I'm usually to be found with my nose buried in a book ... unlike Mike Gatting, whose nose has been found buried in a ball (ouch!).

Actually Gatt is more of a tapes man, and the skipper did me the signal honour after the Sri Lanka tour of lending me his precious set of *Blake's Seven* — though I'm afraid it was a case of *Blake's Six* after Nikki accidentally (or so she

said) recorded one of Keith Floyd's cookery programmes over it. Not that I haven't got a fair
amount of time for Keith in his capacity as drinks-
tray carrier and emergency wicket-keeper for the
Taverners, but it can hardly be said to have helped
matters.

It would be unfair of me to go into any more
details of Nikki's many shortcomings at this stage,
as I'm under contract to tell the story chapter and
verse in the pages of a tabloid newspaper as a way
of financing my divorce – a brilliant deal arranged
through the good offices of my manager Ray
Poole. Let's just say that one good thing *did* come
out of my marriage to Nikki – it's made me
immune to Sledging. When the likes of Merv
Hughes squats in front of me at silly mid-on and
mutters, 'Do you know who's screwing your wife
this minute, mate?', I'm now able to look him
squarely in his ugly mug and reply, 'Yes, mate –
Spamhead!'

JACQUI

The first time I set eyes on Jacqui I was knocked
over – literally! I was up a ladder at the time
engaged in some promotional work for Duraflex
at the Chesterfield Festival, whereupon Jacqui
swans into the tent carrying some bowls of picky
bits, fails to see me and sends me flying! Result:

Dave Podmore left looking like he's the target of one of Spamhead's Bombay Mix-ocets! Jacqui immediately burst into a fit of giggles, and I too had seen the funny side by the close of play that night, when I accompanied Jacqui on a relaxed stroll round the boundary as she collected up discarded sponsors' 3-D glasses.

What's great about Jacqui is that she recognizes the little boy in me, as when I engineered a meeting between her and Nikki at a Sunday League game, I forget where. I lit the blue touch paper by telling Nikki that the new Personality Girl in my life spelt her name J-A-K-K-I and stood back to enjoy the fireworks! I wasn't disappointed, and I'm happy to report that it wasn't Jacqui who needed treatment from the St John's Ambulance boys at the end of the copycat-fight!

Jacqui was, and is, my best friend (better not let the dogs see this page!) and at the time of writing is working closely with Ray Poole, finalizing details of my benefit arrangements with Durham. With that and the divorce from Nikki, the ship of my personal life will be back on a sure footing again. And then who knows? The patter of more tiny Pods perchance? The Great 12th Man taking on 'New Man' duties? Watch this space!*

* See page 143, sadly

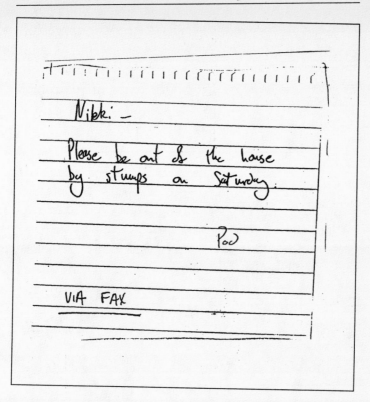

Nikki: —

Please be out of the house by stumps on Saturday.

Pod

VIA FAX

(a) Breaking the news to Nikki. I tried to let her down gently with an idea I borrowed from 'Faxy' Fowler.

> My Dear Selina,
> Just to say that I was absolutely
> désolé to have re-arranged your features with a delivery
> which, with hindsight, may have erred on the brisk
> side of lively. Here's looking forward to raising a glass
> of something acceptable with you in the not-too-distant.
> Yours Ever,
> The Pod-Man

(b) The missive your humble scribe penned to Selina Scott
after 'The Incident'. It's not giving away too many secrets
when I say that Lubo gave me a bit of a hand on the
finer points!

14

JOHNNERS . . . AGGERS . . . BLOWERS . . . BLOOPERS!

Now that I'm something of a senior figure in the game, it's hardly surprising that I should be asked to give the listening public the benefit of my views on the England team playing in any given test match, and more to the point, what's wrong with them.

This used to be entrusted to such legendary seasoned campaigners as Fred Trueman and Trevor Bailey. But then BBC bosses noticed that said legends were going 'soft', in other words starting to cast a benign and twinkling eye over the current crop. Fred, in particular, was acknowledging that, yes, perhaps they *were* faster bowlers, more technically correct batsmen and better fielders than in days of yore. Bert Yore of Sussex he was talking about, picked to play in the Sixth Test against the Windies at the Oval in 1939 and unlucky not to get a trot on account of World War II being declared. The usual short-sighted marketing thinking, I say – the powers that be could have turned it into a Timeless Test and not let it finish until 1945. Imagine the gate receipts!

So, when Radio Five Live, or Radio Three Live as it was then, rang to ask would I consider injecting some new blood into *Test Match Special* by joining the panel of such oracles as Jonathan Agnew and Mike Selvey, my garage door went up faster than Dickie Bird's finger when he wants to get back to his half-finished jigsaw!

Those of you who like to listen to the *TMS* commentary while watching the telly with the sound turned down have probably noticed something a bit strange. The thirty-second gap between what you see on the screen and how it's described on the radio. In particular you'd have been confused by Corky's hat-trick at Old Trafford last year, thinking he actually got six wickets in six balls – Richardson, Hooper, Junior Murray and three other coloured blokes who looked just like them!

Step forward the man responsible – D. V. Podmore, Esquire. This 'time delay' to give it its correct broadcasting terminology, was instigated as a direct result of my notorious debut as a member of the *TMS* team. I guess it was first-night nerves, or thinking too much about when I could make my first remark about cake. Whatever the reason, this is what caused the BBC switchboards to be jammed that fateful morning:

And Capel now starts his run-up . . . comes in to bowl from the Radcliffe Road End . . . with his great big hairy cock hanging out . . . erm, bowling *round* the wicket now I should say . . . ooh, blooming Ada, that didn't come out quite right . . .

When the laughter in the commentary box had died down, round about four o'clock the following afternoon, everybody was extremely sympathetic, saying it could happen to anyone et cetera – though I did find a double Andrex and two grapefruit taped suggestively to the front of my car when I finally slunk out of the ground that night, put there I discovered later by that tireless joker Don Mosey!

Well, the following 'bloopers' tell you that it did indeed happen to them too, and Ray Poole is even now compiling a tape in aid of my benefit, of some of the *TMS* classic 'out-takes' you never heard!

'And it's an absolutely glorious morning here at Old Trafford, especially now Johnners has kicked the bucket . . . er, I mean I can see several *buses* making their way along the Warwick Road . . .'

'Call that crowd misbehaviour? In my day we'd have had that dress off her and the entire dressing-room'd be queuing up waiting to take turns, with Boycs going in Number One! . . . er, I mean, I just despair, I really do.'

'This chocolate gateau looks like some disabled tribeswoman from Bongo-land made it with her feet . . . *and* it tastes like shit – or rather *Mmm!* Thank you Mrs Warburton!'

'And Lara strokes *the most delightful* pair of tits! . . . Off-drive . . .'

The difference being of course, that they were allowed to carry on broadcasting. Muggins here, who gave them Licence to Bloop, has had to pitch his media tent elsewhere (see Chapter 10). But I'm not complaining. I hope you all die of a flesh-eating disease . . . I mean, more power to your elbows, gentlemen!

THE DAVE PODMORE MASTERCLASS

15

THAT'S A VERY GOOD QUESTION!

Just about the most exciting development of late in the marketing of the game (setting aside Pod Noodles, the energy snack on the verge of being patented – just a last-minute rebalancing of the chemicals and it's green-light time!) is the Celebrity Cricket Evening. This consists of much-loved legends with compatible nicknames – 'Beef and Lamb In A Stew' (Botham and Lamb) and 'Tom and Viv Hit It Off' (Graveney and Richards) spring to mind – touring the country, filling up otherwise empty theatres and bridging that awkward cricket-free time zone between the end of the season and the start of panto.

Thirsty audiences turn up in their hordes to quaff heartily from bottles labelled 'Nostalgia', 'Tales of Derring-Do', 'Good Fellowship' and 'Fart Jokes', and Dave Podmore has been privileged to sit in on several of these extravaganzas when one of the regular celebs is incapacitated for one reason or another (generally the latter!!).

Here then are some highlights of my appearance on the recent 'Judge Hangs Lamb For a Sheep' tour, for those who couldn't be there, or the skinflints among you unwilling to shell out the piffling twenty quid to have a damn good night out and see some really excellent footage of me clock-golfing and fly-fishing with Lamby on the River Bure. Not to mention the people who got their money back that night in Guildford after some nark reported me to the Race Relations Board and had the show closed down ... and they talk about Sweden being a police state!

Well, there's no malarkey about Correctness in this book, so yah boo the Do-Gooders! What you have to imagine is the spontaneous bursts of applause and gales of laughter that greeted every one of our off-the-cuff utterances, especially those pertaining to our friends from the sub-Continent!

QUESTION *(from man in grey-and-pink dia-mond-patterned jumper)*:
Has Pod worked out a way to deal with Shane Warne?

ANSWER: Whoo! Tough one to start. I've been watching a lot of tapes of the guy and I think you'll find the answer's to be found in his use of sun-block: if there's just a small dab on each cheek it means the match isn't televised and you should be safe for the afternoon . . . if his face looks like he's just wolfed down a cornet you're in the brown stuff good and deep!

QUESTION *(from man with BOAC airline bag on the empty chair next to him)*:
What's the most bizarre umpiring decision Pod's ever seen on the cricket field?

ANSWER: Well if you're talking abroad – any decision ever made in Pakistan, obviously, where they don't seem to have the letters 'L', 'B' and 'W' in their alphabet . . . let alone 'W' and 'C'! Here, it would have to be old Detective-Inspector Plewsy, 'the long finger of the law'. I can see Judgey's face going all red as he remembers that time he was on course for a 'Fastest Televised' in the Sunday League. The Judge Man had reached 49 in 27 balls and reckoned he had the Hyundai Pony as good as in the car-port when P. C. Plew chutneyed him – causing everyone on the park except the batsman (who vacated the crease muttering 'West Midlands' he thought it was such a wrongful verdict) to comprehensively p*** themselves in a not entirely sympathetic nor significantly dignified fashion!

QUESTION *(from man with spots of dried blood on collar where it meets his neck)*:
Would Pod have taken Phil Tufnell on the last England tour?

ANSWER: 'Tuffers' would definitely be in my side. Form is temporary, class is permanent – and you can quote me on that! Look at his accuracy record on that last tour of Australia. He was under extreme pressure in the hotel room that afternoon, Hotel Security trying to force their way in, and what does he do? He throws a bedside lamp, a minibar, a Gideon Bible and a TV set out the window. He landed each one on the same spot. Two went that way . . . two went on with the arm . . . sheer talent. I'd like to see Richard Illingworth do that with hotel furniture because quite frankly I don't think he's up to it!

While we're at it, I know you're all bursting to hear my views on the Test Selectors, so here goes. I'll be honest and say that as far as D. V. Podmore's concerned, they've let the country down. So what I'd do is, I'd drag them out of the Long Room and take them up to Traitor's Gate in a cart and have 'em hung drawn and quartered . . . then I'd have their entrails displayed across the Nursery End and their eyes pecked out by ravens. I can see one or two of you looking a bit pale, but I'm very sorry, I happen to feel a bit strongly about this. And if that didn't work I'd go for – call me old-fashioned – something like piano wire or battery acid injected into the veins, hopefully perpetrating a slow and painful death. And then I'd fine 'em 30% of their match fees.

QUESTION (*from man with Peter Willey moustache*):
Does Pod have any cricketing superstitions?

ANSWER: Whenever possible, I always try and remember to have a ball in my hand when I run up to bowl – did you see that West Indian guy last season loping in, all flailing arms and grinning gobful of teeth but no cherry?! And then they call them the most fearsome attack in the world and *us* a joke! 'Oh no man,' he says when Dickie Bird points out this little detail in his own inimitable manner, 'I must have left de dam' thing behind with me stash!'

Fifteen minute interval to allow applause, laughter and tears to subside.

126

But seriously, I know from my postbag that there's something lots of you do at home when you're watching a Test, and that's turn your back on the screen and go into the kitchen or to the lav – and more often than not that brings on a wicket. Well I'll let you into a little secret – we do it too! I remember a few years back when the New Zealand lads were compiling one of their 700-odds and there was the England Twelfth Man, Ted Dexter, Fletch and John Major all piling into the Gents at once to try and expedite the situation!

One superstition I treat very respectfully indeed is 'Nelson' and I take a leaf out of David Shepherd's book when the total hits 111, 222 and so on, hopping up and down. I find it's not only a useful bit of exercise (especially if Daffy, Stewie and I have been chutneying the local tandoori the night before – which has been known to happen!) but if you find out where the cameras are and angle your feet in that direction when you hop, you can slip in a couple of endorsements on the soles of your boots!

Apart from that the only hard and fast superstition I try and adhere to is, 'Never play against a certain collection of gentlemen calling themselves the Pakistanis.'

QUESTION *(from woman wearing white ankle socks)*:
Who does Pod think is the greatest Ambassador for the game?

ANSWER: David Gower, no question. If you're on tour and having to get all poshed up and go to an Embassy bash, Lubo's the man you want to be sitting next to. Suave, polished, diplomatic and he'll always tell you which fork to use . . . when you want to stick it in one of the other lads' ears!

QUESTION *(from man with jet-black hair and wearing driving gloves)*:
What advice would Pod give to youngsters considering taking up the game?

ANSWER: Don't bother, try something else instead, there are enough 43-year-olds trying to earn a crust already.

QUESTION *(from woman in neck-brace)*:
Would Pod like to share his views with us on the Pakistanis?

ANSWER: Looks like you've faced one of Wasim's Wrong 'Uns yourself, dear! But it gives me no pleasure at all ladies and gentlemen, to have to say that out there, ball-tampering is a way of life. It runs through their society from bottom to top – if you think Benazir Bhutto grows those long fingernails just to look good at Summit Conferences then I'm afraid you're living in a fool's paradise my friend!

Though I have to say I have to exclude my old mate Javed Miandad from the general criticism. Javed's come up trumps turning out in charity matches for the Taverners and we've shared many a Champagne Moment together (a Fanta Moment for Javed, obviously). That afternoon in 1982 he was going for the winning run off the bowling of Fred Dineage and he collides mid-pitch with Bob Carolgees and Spit the Dog!! The only tragedy was it was before the invention of the camcorder! Plus the fact that we lost the match and couldn't afford the Sunshine Coach for another year of course, but that's cricket.

QUESTION *(from man in wheelchair)*:
Does Pod have any regrets?

ANSWER: Strewth Judgey, look at the state of this! He's more permanently legless than I am! No offence, sir. Well as they say in the song: *'Je Ne Regrette Reen'* . . . well I do regret Reen actually, she was that barmaid at the Saracen's Head in Nuneaton . . . but I look at it like this – every so often you have to be big enough to hold up your hand and take a decision in life and perhaps look back on it with a bit of a wry smile. And I mean you can't rewrite the clock and, as I say at the end of the day, you've got to be able to get out of bed and look at yourself in the mirror so obviously as I say – No. Yes.

QUESTION *(from another man in grey-and-pink diamond-patterned jumper)*:
How would Pod like to be remembered?

ANSWER: As somewhat the worse for wear! Talking of which, Judgey ... ! That concludes the evening's entertainment, so goodnight everybody, God bless, safe journey home ... which you most certainly will have if you're driving a vehicle from Ray Poole (Nissan) Hinckley. Nice people – nice prices!

16

TOWARDS THE MILLENNIUM

This is where Pod makes himself public enemy number one with readers of the *Guardian* and other up-the-bum organs of Political Correctitude. I'm afraid that we have now reached the point in the game of cricket where we have to ask ourselves very seriously indeed whether we are prepared to let the game follow so many other British institutions down the drain or whether we are prepared to do something. Here are a few modest proposals of my own.

TOOL UP THE UMPS

Can any cricket lover look himself in the mirror and honestly say that it's any longer fair or reasonable to deny our umpires the protection of semi-automatic firearms? I realize that to the traditionalist the idea of Nigel Plews packing a rod seems all wrong. But you have to bear in mind that there are a lot of important games due to be played at Headingley next year, plus the fact that our friends the Pakistanis will be with us again before long. Is a slight bulge in the white coat and a small risk of accidents such a high price to pay for peace of mind? Pod thinks not.

The truth is you have to move with the times. It makes me smile now to think of those so-called purists who rubbished coloured clothing when it first came in. I expect there's a few red faces among them now that the AXA Equity & Law League supporters strip is the premier choice leisure-wear for lads and dads throughout the UK marketplace. I'm afraid you can't stop progress any more than you can stop Christopher Martin Jenkins doing his impressions.

And I'm not sure that the introduction of weapons is such a big step anyway. Nigel Plews has been 'handling iron' since he was a pink-arsed bobby on the beat. It's an open secret on the circuit that Roy Palmer carried heat at Heanor during the miners' strike of '84. And we all know what happens when Jack Hampshire puts on that short-sleeved nylon shirt with the walkie-talkie holster and Highway Patrol shades – everyone behaves good as gold, that's what!

As I say though, in my experience, lapses of discipline are always down to the player not knowing where he stands with the umpire. Ball-tampering, stump abuse, sledging, spitting in an opponent's face and scratching 'cheating black bastard' on his bonnet – these are all part and parcel of the grand old game. But a line has to be drawn in the sand somewhere and I think the umpire should do it with a shooter.

Take my own alleged breach of sporting etiquette. It was a very minor incident (typically distorted by the media, of course). But no way would I have continued the horseplay with the stump for as long as I did if Umpire Balderstone had been 'carrying'. Nor would I have made the leg-pulling remarks about his domestic situation; the damage would not have been done to the pitch or the Duraflex tent; none of the girls in the office would have got hurt; Daffy's Mazda wouldn't have needed a respray and, who knows, the county might have got away with a warning instead of a three-year ban from the competition. *Pod Erat Demonstrandum*, as Phil Edmonds once remarked after I'd shoved the crossword dictionary up his jacksie.

FOREIGNERS

I don't deliberately set out to get up the nasal passages of the chattering classes, it just seems to

133

happen that way. Mike Brearley would probably reckon it's because I had a hand-shandy off my grannie when I was two months old. I think it's because I speak as I find. And I find quite a lot of things to be a sick joke, to be honest.

Foreigners playing for England, for example. Whoever thought that one up wants taking out and shooting. Don't get me wrong, I've got nothing against the TCCB, I just don't like foreigners pretending to be English.

If you look up Alec Stewart in the *Cricketers' Who's Who*, it says he was born in Merton. Now, I've got a lot of time for Stewie, he's a great guy and I am sure what he says is true. (I hope it is for his sake anyway.) The point is, though, how do we *know* he was born in Merton? How do we know he wasn't born in, say, Karachi? It's not difficult to produce a birth certificate if you know the right people and you can do all sorts with make-up, as I've discovered from working in pantomime the last few winters.

Obviously the system needs looking at. My solution is a very simple one: compulsory DNA finger-printing for all first-class cricketers.

As we know, DNA tests aren't 110% reliable, so I propose a series of measures which would provide a back-up system, that way we won't have any accidents. First of all, a proper blood test followed by examination of family dental

records going back, say three generations. Personally, I'm not in favour of measuring the size of a
player's 'crown jewels' – you're a sitting target for
one of I. T. Botham's celebrated practical jokes for
one thing. But the final decision on that would
have to rest with the England manager.

I do think though that we should look very
closely at a new technique currently being developed in America. It's a highly intricate process
whereby the sportsman is placed in a darkened
room and played a selection of foreign national
anthems. Hypersensitive pads attached to his body
can detect the slightest swelling of pride in the
chest region or lump-formation in the throat. It's a
foolproof way of finding out where a guy's loyal-
ties lie, but unfortunately it is still in its infancy and
therefore very expensive. I have designed a much
cheaper process which could be put into service
more or less immediately. You give the prospective
England player a set of head-phones and play him
a tape of Will Carling reading Kenneth Branagh's
speech from *Henry V* – if his pulse doesn't quicken
instantly, you know you're dealing with a self-
serving journeyman who isn't fit to tie Angus
Fraser's boot-laces and he wants to get on the
boat and go straight back where he came from.

The whole vetting procedure (including blood-
bonding and virgin sacrifice) would take two

weeks at the most – we'd be able to get rid of the rotten apples, put a stop to all the speculation and get on with the game. I'd stick with Smithy though, and Hicky looks a prospect.

KEYS OF THE KINGDOM

I must have seen fifty pre-match pitch reports on TV last summer. Guess how many sets of English car keys I saw being stuck in the turf? None. How is an England team supposed to feel when they see that sort of thing coming from their own television channel. If you were a Springbok or a Kiwi sat in front of the dressing-room telly and you saw Boycs whip out his Volkswagen fob and sink it in the track – well you'd feel ten feet tall, wouldn't you? So instead of bending over backwards to make life easy for our opponents, why don't we help ourselves for a change? Let's stick to British cars for British commentators and let's see a few more Rover and Mondeo logos wiggling about in Harry Brind's marl.

A SPINSTER'S PARADISE

I've given my life to this grand old game and I get very worried when I hear about plans to muck around with it. You hear so-called experts in the media saying things like the Championship's the most poorly attended sporting contest anywhere in the world, the standard's not very high, and since even the players think there's too many games we might as well do away with the whole thing. I think that tells you all you need to know about the standard of patriotism in the media.

To me, county cricket sums up all those good, old fashioned English values like the village green, the spinster setting her stall out to go to Evensong – putting her bike there or thereabouts in the fog – and probably having a laugh and a warm beer with the vicar afterwards. The media can sneer if they want but I happen to have a lot of time for that kind of thing. If progress means altering the Championship then, frankly, gentlemen of the Test and County Cricket Board, you can keep progress!

Having said that, it would probably make more sense to split it up into five zonal divisions and play the matches at night to get more marketing, but apart from that, my message to the powers that be would be a very simple one: LEAVE WELL ALONE.

THE SEXUAL AXA

We've already seen coloured clothing attract huge numbers of the young, fashionable set to the AXA Equity & Law Sunday league matches. I don't think there's much doubt that, for the female fans, it's what's *inside* the coloured clothing which appeals more than anything else. I think we would be fools unto ourselves if we were to ignore the commercial implications of that.

I don't want to be indelicate but, frankly, a woman likes to look at a cricketer's backside; it's a fact of life. When I was watching Andy Moles see off the shine on a greentop at Neath last April, I couldn't fail to be impressed by the number of young lovelies chanting 'Buns out for the girls, Molesy'. I knew immediately there was a marketing lesson to be learned there. Details of a similar incident at Hove subsequently reached my ears via the dressing-room grapevine. Apparently Eddie Hemmings opened a tub of Haagen Dazs in the Dyno-Rod tent on a hot afternoon last back-end. One of the TV South weather girls got so steamed up she ripped open Eddie's shirt, uncovered herself and went completely berserk with a spoon, poor lass. So it's useless to pretend that sexual attraction doesn't play a major part in the forty-over game. Rather than denying the sexual revolution, we should be embracing it.

That's why Ray Poole and I have designed a revolutionary new trouser for exclusive use in Sunday league matches. It's been conceived with the ladies' tastes specifically in mind and will form part of the new 'Pod Collection' range of clothing which will be available shortly. The 'AXA-pant' has a transparent polyurethane 'window' in the seat of the trouser providing a rare and sensuous erotic experience for the female fan. Whether her heart-throb is patrolling the covers or crouching in the gully, the AXA-pant will keep a girl smiling on all but the coldest of two-sweater days (when a clothes-peg could be used to hitch the sweater up). It also opens up an exciting new era of prime advertising space.

I'd also extend the AXA to 75 overs a side (playing the second dig by candle-light would create an intimate romantic atmosphere). Sledging, kidology, ball-tampering, why not? If we want to get the youngsters along, cricket has to be marketed as the 'in' thing to do? Ray Poole has been working on a state-of-the-art advertising campaign, hopefully fronted by Sir Tim Rice, with the slogan 'AXA Equity and Law Sunday League cricket – it's happening!' I don't think it'll be too long before we see grounds packed to the rafters with funky, way out kids 'doing their own thing' as they say.

So Pod's solution to saving the noble old game from going down the pan and bringing it into the twenty-first century is lots of sex, tool up the umps and no foreigners. I'm sorry if that gets up the pipes of certain so-called media journalists and television commentators (who, by the way, would be out of a job if it wasn't for us) and I'm sorry if it offends readers of the *Guardian* and the *Independent* (most of whom have probably never had a job in the first place). Above all, sorry to Iris who does the teas at Hinckley, I was out of order and I hope the bat with the hand-painted portrait of Dave Podmore on it makes up for it.

THE DAVE PODMORE MASTERCLASS

17

AFTERWORD:
HAVING SAID THAT

Well, there it is. A voyage round the coral reefs, the rocky inlets and the turbulent waters of the Isle of Pod (not forgetting the intermittently painful shingles!). Whatever the future holds for Dave Podmore, the important thing is that he can look back on what he's done and know that he's achieved it not by bowing and scraping and going to Cambridge University, not by scratching someone's back to get into Oadby Golf Club – which hasn't the facilities they've got at South Hinckley anyway. No, he did it by sweat and graft and bowling with a boot full of blood. In the words of a certain blue-eyed gent who's still turning out under the name of F. A. Sinatra, Dave Podmore did it my way.

Not that the future hasn't looked on the parky side of bleakish of late. Ray Poole, my manager, decided to plough the profits from my most recent benefits back into the business – his own as it happens, and the police of three Britannic Assurance counties are currently on the lookout for him, together with my ex-fiancée Jacqui who chose to take the Ray Poole shilling – or the Dave Podmore £78,000 with change, to be more accurate.

This means that Mr Bojangles is temporarily closed and my plans for 'Cinderella-Rockerfellas' on the outskirts of Leicester have had to be temporarily put on ice (I can hear that clown Ray's voice now: 'A nightclub on ice, Pod – top idea in its field!') Frankly, I'm well shot of the pair of them.

Trying to come up with a title for this book was no picnic either. Once again it was a case of my face not fitting, and I found out pretty soon that if your name doesn't happen to be Vic Marks you can forget calling your book *Marks Out of Eleven*. *Mike Brearley on the Art of Captaincy* . . . *Mike Atherton on Captaincy* – both examples of how the Silver Spoon brigade have got things pretty well sewn up. *Lamb to the Slaughter*, *Cardus on Cricket*, *Hick 'n' Dilley Circus* – all out of bounds for the likes of me. I thought I'd made a breakthrough with *The Dave Podmore Story*, only to find that Martyn Moxon had beaten me to it.

But now the sun's come out, the covers are off, and play will be resuming after tea all being well.

Dave Junior is almost seventeen and a credit to his old man – and, judging by the way he burst all the balloons at our local Harvester the other day, he's got a pretty good eye as well! He's a bit of a late developer, but I've no doubt in due course he'll be going for trials at Derby like two generations of Podmores before him. And in the event of a successful outcome there's a dream present waiting for him on a certain forecourt – a gleaming new Micra from Keith Endicott (Nissan) of Wyggeston.

And as I say – I've always got the dogs.

Self-Portrait of a Cricketer

Appendix 1

DAVE PODMORE'S
FANTASY XIs

PRACTICAL JOKES

1) BOGUS TEST SELECTION

There's a guy who works at Ceefax who, for a suitable fee, is prepared to flash up the victim's name on TV for ten minutes on a Sunday morning – at the exact moment you ring him up and congratulate him on being chosen for the squad. This call should be a quickie, to give him enough time to ring round his family and friends with the good news!

2) MOUTH-TO-MOUTH RESUSCITATION ON THE PITCH

A great one when it comes off. You bowl short, and your partner-in-crime at the other end hoists it off the shoulder of his bat into his face and 'collapses'! Once at Grace Road, Spamhead did such a realistic impression of being dead (judicious application of boot-whitener to the fizzog) that David Constant passed out and had to be given treatment on the pitch himself!

3) MONDEO MADRAS
Sponsored car 'Gotchas' would make a Fantasy XI on their own, but my favourite is dal in the brake fluid, followed closely by the slow burner: ten quids' worth of vindaloo in the glove box. Very effective if your victim is setting out to impress an eligible Personality Girl, by taking corners too fast!

4) PLASTIC HAIR-LICE/CRABS IN THE JOCK-STRAP
Obtainable from Ho-Ho-Ho Chi Minh Novelties, Upper Parliament Street, Nottingham. Also stocks the Charles Colvile Mask – clears a dressing-room in seconds!

5) ACTIVATING THE SPRINKLER SYSTEM
A memorable opening night at my Mr Bojangles venture in Ashby-de-la-Zouch turned into an un-forgettable one – Ninja-Man climbed on Beef's shoulders and Goughy supported the pair of them as Ninja-Man held up a fag lighter to achieve the above effect. In the resulting cascade Goughy slipped over and was out for a season and a half, but it was worth it for the huge laughs!

6) THE BAD NEWS FAX (see page 66)
Unfortunately this one has been known to back-
fire, as when I faxed Nikki telling her to be out of
the house by such-and-such a time. She thought it
was a gag and was still there when I arrived for a
relaxed evening with Jacqui. Result: broken glass
everywhere and several cut paws. As far as I'm
concerned the maltreatment of dogs should be
punishable by death.

7) THE ELECTRIC FIRE IN THE TEAM
BATH
Ideally unplugged a split-second before it's thrown
in, so the bars are still glowing for maximum
effect!

8) THE NAUGHTY LUBO
An ultra-realistic lipstick-stained used condom.
Slip it into a team-mate's back pocket and wait
till his wife does the laundry! Three marriages have
gone west to my certain knowledge thanks to this
little beauty, though in its defence they were in a
rocky state already.

9) THE BUCKING BRONCO
Fastening a pal to the roof of his car with 'spiders'
then pushing it down a hill. You've got a colleague
concealed under the steering wheel controlling it,
but the victim doesn't know that!

10) THE BOTTLE OF SOMETHING UNACCEPTABLE

You've guessed it – when you've got enough 'samples', carefully fill an empty wine bottle, re-cork and seal, then present it to the one of your bon-viveur, hopefully Oxbridge-educated team-mates. Should be stored at room temperature!

11) ORANGE/SUSPENDERS/ROPE HIDDEN IN THE KIT-BAG

Don't really understand this one but apparently it's a big favourite with the Middlesex and Surrey boys.

SNACKS

With so many top-notch snacks vying to catch the eye (and the taste-buds!) of the Selectors, Pod's Fantasy Snack XI is bound to spark controversy, and have *aficionados* debating heatedly in pubs and clubs across the land. That age-old question – Doritos versus Cheesy Wotsits for the coveted Number 5 spot – has by itself caused more dressing-room brawls than I care to think about.

Greybeards talk fondly of the old Nibbits days, arguing they're the Don Bradman of snacks, always giving 110% when they were brought out of the old tin 'snap' box. I'd merely point out that, like the Don, the Nib hasn't had to compete in the modern era, so who knows how he would stand up to a head-to-head fight with Cheese and Onion Discos or Tomato Sauce-flavoured Potato Tubes. Cheesy Wotsits, however, have seen off both such challenges – and, unlike Nibbits, leave your mouth orange without taking the roof off it.

So, let battle commence, and remember that, just this once, Pod's decision is final. There's no place here for the whingeing 'No-Eating-Between Meals' voice of the Establishment!

1) CRINKLE-CUT ROYSTERS
There, it's done. If you want to argue about it, we'll sort it out in the car park afterwards. Sure

they're young, but they've shown immense promise.

2) READY SALTED CRISPS

Another controversial selection. No question, Salt'n'Shake is a fine, fine crisp – but it also has a maverick quality that leads me to suspect you couldn't always rely on it in a crisis. I once bought a packet that contained twenty-seven sachets of salt and only one crisp. Where would that leave you in the tea interval on the fifth day with another 37 overs to bowl or risk a post-match fine? No, to shore up the snack batting with one wicket down, Pod backs ready salted crisps to get the job done.

3) CHIPSTICKS

Just get The Nod over their salt'n'vinegar Hula Hoop rivals for the Number 3 berth. Both give savoury satisfaction, but Chippies shave it for durability.

4) DRY ROASTED PEANUTS

The Robin Smith of the nut world – originally brought in from overseas, but now selflessly giving all to post-match drinks accessorizing.

5) FRAZZLES

Every time. 'Why not Quavers?' I hear you cry. 'What have they done to be left out *again*?'

Because, in my book, they're lightweight, insubstantial, and in no way suitable for the pressure-cooker atmosphere of Test Match cricket. (Coincidentally, Frazzles' savoury bacon odour is remarkably similar to the interior smell of Hicky's car.)

6) PORK SCRATCHINGS

A safe pair of hands behind the Chipsticks. And you want to talk E-Numbers? They've got 'em to spare!

7) TWIGLETS

The Guvnor. Every team needs an all-rounder and, for me, Twiglets fill the multi-purpose snack role to perfection. Open a packet in the dressing-room and they'll stick around until tea-time on day three if the situation demands. But, if you're in a hurry to get through the opposition, Twiglets will stop the gap between lunch and dinner time after time. If they renamed them 'Capel-ets' they wouldn't be far wrong.

8) BOMBAY MIX

Here's one in the eye for the critics who say that Pod's totally blinkered to anything but home-grown Brit-snacks. Wrong – I've got a lot of time for the sub-continent when it comes to snack craftsmanship, and for that reason I include these guys. It's a wily, crafty snack which catches you out with its beguiling blend of spice and chilli time and again. Also good for pouring over mates' heads (see Chapter 9).

9) EXTRA-HOT TORTILLA CHIPS
Fiery, temperamental, but always on for a diarrhoea finish.

10) RITZ CRACKERS
Dependable workhorse of a snack, big-hearted, invariably first up at the death to say 'Skipper, eat me'.

11) MONSTER MUNCH
I'm all for giving new snacks a try, and, for my money (27p), Munchy has the potential to be around for quite a time to come. Has the added advantage of amusing monster shapes which you can flick at Athers when he's trying to read the latest Umberto Eco!

I know I'll probably have upset the purists and if so I'm sorry. Some snacks, like Macadamia Nuts and Pretzel Bits are already bubbling under, and I'm sure we'll hear a lot more of them in the future. But I think you'll agree I have assembled a well-balanced savoury side – in other words, your humble Selector can get through all eleven bags at one sitting!

FILMS

1) *Die Hard*
2) *Die Hard 2*
3) *Die Hard with a Vengeance*
4) *Old Habits Die Hard*
5) *Top Gun*
6) *Where Eagles Dare*
7) *Howards End 2: The Working-Class Strikes Back* (with Dolph Lundgren and Jean-Claude Van Damme, available on video only)
8) *Death Wish*
9) *Emmanuelle*
10) *Rocky*
11) *Watership Down*

Last Man In might surprise some of you, but this gentle rabbit saga appeals to the romantic and mystical side of my nature. I could, and indeed have, been known to watch the tape over and over again – so much so that during my season with Sussex the theme song 'Bright Eyes' was played over the PA system when I came on to bowl, lulling the crowd into a pleasant drowsiness.

This gave me a marketing idea which is still under consideration with the TCCB: to 'play on' an incoming batsman with an appropriate tune like they used to do on 'Parkinson'. Examples which spring to mind are 'Nowhere Man' (Craig White), 'Hello Goodbye' (Mark Ramprakash), 'Ten Green Bottles' (David Gower).

FANTASY BOOKS XI

1) *The Dogs of War* – Jack Higgins
2) *The Plague Dogs* – Len Deighton
3) *War of the Dogs* – Dirk Pitt
4) *The Book of the Alsatian* – Time Life Inc.
5) *Snowflake, Story of an Exmoor Pony.* The first book I ever read and still the best by a country mile.

To be honest, I'm not a great one for books. So as I'm still six short I'll make up the numbers with magazines.

6) *The Puzzler*
7) *Association of Alsatian Owners and Breeders Newsletter*
8) *Dog*

I would probably be able to pick up the last three on the way to the ground.

Appendix 2

THE STATS
(reproduced by permission of *The Cricketers' Who's Who*)

NAME:	David Vincent Podmore
ROLE:	Bits-and–Pieces Player; Roving Ambassador for Cricket during close season
BORN:	29 September 1953, Mansfield Notts.
HEIGHT:	5ft 11ins (inc helmet)
WEIGHT:	Variable, depending on whether or not I've been out for a blow-out the night before with a certain I. T. Botham!
COUNTY:	Leics, Derbys, Sussex, Notts, Glamorgan, Gloucs, Northants, Somerset, Leics, hopefully Durham
BENEFIT YEAR:	1974, 1977, 1981, 1984 (twice), 1987, 1990, 1993, hopefully 1997
TEST DEBUT:	1991/92 Sri Lanka

TESTS:	1
ONE-DAY INTERNATIONALS:	3 (4 according to Wisden – took the field disguised as Chris Broad)
1000 RUNS:	0
FIRST-CLASS 50s:	0
FIRST-CLASS 100S:	0
FIRST-CLASS 200s:	0
FIRST-CLASS 37s:	1
5-WICKET INNINGS:	0
10-WICKET INNINGS:	0
THINGS THAT GIVE ME A BIGGER KICK THAN VISITING SICK KIDDIES:	0
BEST BOWLING PERFORMANCE:	3 for 62, vs Combined Universities 1991 (should have been four, but a certain gentleman whose initials are not unadjacent to I.T.B. rained on my parade by decking a sitter!)
OVERSEAS TOURS:	Under-14s Tour of West Indies; India/Sri Lanka 1991/92; Cambodian Breweries XI

FANCY DRESS RECORDS: Winning costumes at the Christmas parties on England tours 1971–94 (excluding Rest of the World matches):

1971/72	Brian Luckhurst (*Lawrence of Arabia*)
1973/74	Tony Greig (*Lawrence of Arabia*)
1974/75	Mike Denness (*Hiawatha*)
1976/77	Geoff Miller (*Lawrence of Arabia*)
1978/79	I. T. Botham (*Punk Rock*)
1980/81	Allan Lamb (*Diana Ross*)
1982/83	David Gower (*Old-fashioned typical English Raj Colonel*)
1984/85	John Thicknesse (*Jiminy Cricket*)
1986/87	Henry Blofeld (*Yootha Joyce – TV's Mildred*)
1988/89	Chris Broad (*Lawrence of Arabia*)
1990/91	Charles Colvile (*Himself*)
1991/92	Dave Podmore (*Lawrence of Arabia*)

N.B. According to the new ICC ruling, Eddie Hemmings's Bet Lynch (Pochefstroom 1989/90) is no longer ranked as first class.

DISCIPLINARY HEARINGS:

Authority	Findings
TCCB	Totally ridiculous
Leics. CCC	Sad
Glamorgan CCC	Sick
British Transport Police	Small-minded
Notts. CCC	Pathetic after all I've done (see % table)
Leicester City Council	Pending
Pochefstroom Assizes	Utterly vindicated

PERCENTAGE EFFORT GIVEN IN FIRST CLASS CRICKET:

Team	Per cent
Leicestershire	110
Derbyshire	150
Nottinghamshire	200
Leics. (benefit year)	99.9
Sussex (divorce year)	47
England	2000
Average (day in, day out):	199.99 per cent

POD'S NICKNAMES:
Pod
Poddy
Podders
Podd (Glamorgan)
Pod Man
The Pod Man
Poderoony
Poddington
Leonard Woolf (given to me by Mike Brearley. Crazy guy. That man needs his head examined – by himself!!)